THE OPEN UNIVERSITY
A SCIENCE FOUNDATION COURSE

C000280840

UNITS 17–18 THE CHEMISTRY OF CARBON COMPOUNDS

THE SCIENCE FOUNDATION COURSE TEAM

Steve Best (Illustrator)
Geoff Brown (Earth Sciences)
Jim Burge (BBC)
Neil Chalmers (Biology)
Bob Cordell (Biology, General Editor)
Pauline Corfield (Assessment Group and
    Summer School Group)
Debbie Crouch (Designer)
Dee Edwards (Earth Sciences; S101 Evaluation)
Graham Farmelo (Chairman)
John Greenwood (Librarian)
Mike Gunton (BBC)
Charles Harding (Chemistry)
Robin Harding (Biology)
Nigel Harris (Earth Sciences, General Editor)
Linda Hodgkinson (Course Coordinator)
David Jackson (BBC)
David Johnson (Chemistry, General Editor)
Tony Jolly (BBC, Series Producer)
Ken Kirby (BBC)
Perry Morley (Editor)
Peter Morrod (Chemistry)
Pam Owen (Illustrator)
Rissa de la Paz (BBC)
Julia Powell (Editor)
David Roberts (Chemistry)
David Robinson (Biology)
Shelagh Ross (Physics, General Editor)

Dick Sharp (Editor)
Ted Smith (BBC)
Margaret Swithenby (Editor)
Nick Watson (BBC)
Dave Williams (Earth Sciences)
Geoff Yarwood (Earth Sciences)

Consultants: Keith Hodgkinson (Physics)
Judith Metcalfe (Biology)
Pat Murphy (Biology)
Irene Ridge (Biology)
Jonathan Silvertown (Biology)

External assessor: F. J. Vine FRS

Others whose S101 contribution has been of
considerable value in the preparation of S102:
Stuart Freake (Physics)
Anna Furth (Biology)
Stephen Hurry (Biology)
Jane Nelson (Chemistry)
Mike Pentz (Chairman and General Editor, S101)
Milo Shott (Physics)
Russell Stannard (Physics)
Steve Swithenby (Physics)
Peggy Varley (Biology)
Kiki Warr (Chemistry)
Chris Wilson (Earth Sciences)

The trace in the front cover illustration shows an analysis of crude oil using the technique of gas chromatography.

The Open University, Walton Hall, Milton Keynes, MK7 6AA.

First published 1988. Reprinted 1989, 1990, 1992, 1993, 1994, 1995, 1996.

Copyright © 1988, 1989, 1995. The Open University.

Designed by the Graphic Design Group of the Open University.

Filmset by Santype International Limited, Salisbury, Wiltshire;
printed by Henry Ling Ltd., at the Dorset Press, Dorchester, Dorset.

ISBN 0 335 16333 5

This text forms part of an Open University Course. For general availability of
supporting material referred to in this text please write to: Open University
Educational Enterprises Limited, 12 Cofferidge Close, Stony Stratford,
Milton Keynes, MK11 1BY, Great Britain.

Further information on Open University Courses may be obtained from the
Admissions Office, The Open University, P.O. Box 48, Walton Hall,
Milton Keynes, MK7 6AB.

STUDY GUIDE

Units 17-18 have been produced as a single entity and comprise this text, two TV programmes, three AV sequences, a molecular model kit and a stereoviewer with filmstrips.

The text is divided into eight main Sections; you should attempt to reach the end of Section 4 by the end of your first week's study.

The first TV programme, 'Organic molecules in action', deals with two industrially important examples of carbon compounds in agricultural and pharmaceutical chemistry as well as some of the techniques used in making carbon compounds from simpler starting substances. It relates particularly to Sections 4, 5 and 6. You will most probably watch this programme before having read the relevant Sections of the text, so we have included some brief notes (Section 9) to place the programme content in context, and you should read these before viewing the programme. If you have the facilities, you may find it particularly useful to record this programme and view it when you reach the appropriate stage in these Units. The other TV programme, 'Man-made macromolecules', deals with the methods used to make the giant molecules that constitute some of the many useful plastic materials that now pervade our lives. It relates particularly to Section 7; there are some additional notes that relate specifically to the programme content in Section 10. You should read these TV notes when you view the programme, whether or not you have read Section 7.

The three AV sequences deal with the various aspects of the phenomenon of isomerism, a concept central to much of this double Unit, and there is one sequence for each of Sections 3, 4 and 5. Although there are no experiments for this pair of Units, your Experiment Kit does contain a molecular model kit; you will need to use this mainly with the AV sequences, but you will find it useful at other times as well. In the Kit there is also a stereoviewer with appropriate filmstrips, again for use mainly with the AV sequences. In addition, for the third AV sequence you will need to obtain a mirror, preferably at least 12 cm × 12 cm (or 12 cm diameter if circular), and some means of holding it vertical. (One possible way would be to use the retort stand, boss and clamp from the Experiment Kit.)

There are a number of Colour Plates at the back of the text. These are used to illustrate particular points in Sections 1, 2, 5 and 7.

You are not expected to memorize the names of individual compounds: you will always be given the structural formulae where they are needed in assignments and examinations. However, you will probably find that some, at least, of the more common names will stick without any conscious effort. To help you, we have included, at the end of the text, a separate Appendix of chemical names* and structures; this also contains, *for interest only*, some information concerning the occurrence, properties and uses of some of the compounds listed. If you find that you are becoming bogged down in the details, and are not clear what you are expected to remember, look at the list of Objectives (pp. 97-8); these tell you the main terms and concepts that you are expected to learn from this pair of Units.

---

* In these Units, we have, with very few exceptions, followed the recommendations of the International Union of Pure and Applied Chemistry (IUPAC) for naming chemical compounds. Where these recommendations have not been unambiguous, we have tended towards the more systematic approach. Where non-systematic names have been adopted, it is either because these are preferred in the IUPAC recommendations, or because they are widely used in industry or biochemistry, or both.

1 INTRODUCTION TO THE CHEMISTRY OF CARBON COMPOUNDS

Imagine, if you can, life as it was a century ago. Perhaps the first thing you would notice would be the drabness, the lack of variety of colour (Plate 1). The new synthetic dyes were still few in number, and they tended to fade rapidly. Likewise, paints had little variety, the pigments used being the traditional ones discovered long before. Clothes were mostly heavy and needed endless attention; it was to be many years before the discovery and exploitation of synthetic fibres brought the promise of 'drip-dry' and 'non-iron'. Dry-cleaning had not been developed commercially and soap was frequently harsh in action. Food had either to be fresh, or preserved by salting, pickling or drying; domestic refrigeration and deep-freezing were far in the future. If a Victorian required surgery, and could afford it, he or she would probably have had the benefit of ether or chloroform as anaesthetics (Figure 1), but their administration was crude, and was not without its own hazards! In addition, the patient might well have succumbed to an infection for which there was a very limited range of drugs.

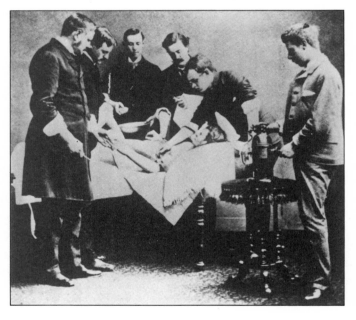

FIGURE 1   An operating theatre during the 1880s. The much improved safety of modern surgical procedures, and the much greater range of medical conditions amenable to surgery, is due to the discovery both of safe general anaesthetics and a wide range of drugs to control post-operative infection.

By contrast, nowadays we take it for granted that we can buy clothes of virtually any colour or shade and that the colour will not fade (Plate 2). Paints can not only be of any colour but are also much more durable. Modern detergents are much more efficient and usually less harmful to fabrics in their action. The production and distribution of food in adequate quantities relies heavily on the use of pesticides to prevent crop destruction, on refrigeration and, of course, on petroleum for transportation, and on plastics for packaging. If we fall ill, we expect that there will be in most cases a suitable drug virtually tailor-made, and we have confidence that, with the use of modern anaesthetics, surgical procedures carry very little risk (Figure 2). With the increased leisure time that many now enjoy, there is a wide range of recreational activities that depend in no small part on synthetic fibres or plastics such as nylon or polyester (Plate 3). Increasingly, the aircraft and automotive industries are replacing metal components with new materials, many of which are based on synthetic polymers* (that is, large molecules formed by the linking together of many smaller ones). The entire development of the modern electrical and electronic industries has

* The synthesis and properties of polymers are discussed in Section 7.

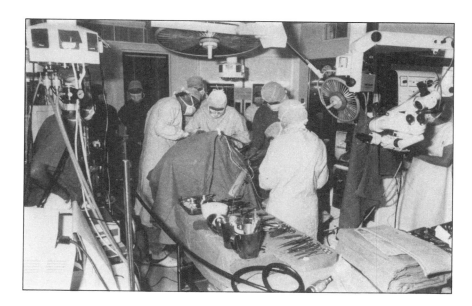

FIGURE 2 A modern operating theatre.

depended on, and continues to depend on, the use of polymers as electrical insulating materials and in the process used for the production of printed circuits and integrated circuits ('silicon chips') (Figure 3). All these changes, and many more, have been brought about through the discovery and exploitation, over the past century, of the chemical and physical properties of carbon compounds.

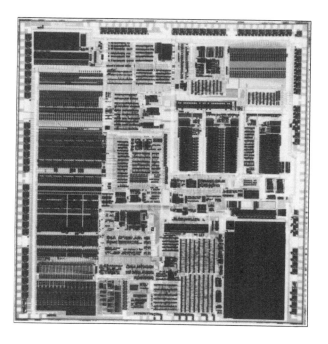

FIGURE 3 The Intel 80386 micro-processor which is used in a wide range of microcomputers. The etching process used to manufacture such integrated circuits is wholly dependent on the use of organic chemical coatings to allow the production of the intricate and complex microscopic circuitry involved. These coatings are formed by the action of ultraviolet radiation, which causes the linking of small molecules to form very large, insoluble ones.

However, while not denying the immense improvement in the quality of life for many millions of people, it is impossible to ignore the fact that many of these developments have had adverse consequences that must be weighed against their advantages. In the case of pharmaceutical products, most people would consider that the benefits to society outweigh the risks. Tragic though it was for the individuals concerned, the recognition of the harmful effects of the drug Thalidomide during the 1960s did not stimulate a public outcry for all new drug development to cease, though it did result in much more stringent requirements for the testing of new drugs. On the other hand, the advantages of DDT as a pesticide are now generally considered to be outweighed by the undesirable side-effects associated with its use, and so in most countries its use has been banned. None the less, for better or for worse, modern life, particularly in the developed countries, relies in large measure on the chemistry of carbon compounds.

ORGANIC CHEMISTRY

HYDROCARBON

MOLECULAR FORMULA

We can go further: the existence of life on this planet is *based* on the chemistry of carbon. The chemistry of life itself—the growth, development and eventual death of every living thing—involves the interaction and reaction of an incredible variety of complex carbon compounds. Indeed the subject originated in the 19th century from 'the study of substances containing carbon that are constituents of or formed from organized bodies', that is the study of substances produced by living organisms—hence the name **organic chemistry**. This term has come to be synonymous with the chemistry of carbon compounds though many such compounds have no connection with living organisms. In these Units the terms 'carbon compounds' and 'organic compounds' will be used interchangeably. Despite the complexity of many of the processes that are involved in the chemistry of life, the application of a relatively small number of basic principles, allied with the use of modern analytical techniques, has enabled scientists to unravel them in remarkable detail.

It is difficult to overestimate the importance of the chemistry of carbon compounds. At the time of writing (1987) well over eight million distinct chemical compounds have been listed by the American Chemical Society's Chemical Abstracts Service. You may be surprised to learn that more than 97% of these contain carbon. Of the order of 100 000 carbon compounds are in common use as, for example, drugs, pesticides, food additives etc. In this pair of Units we can only scratch the surface of the subject. Nevertheless, we hope that in so doing we are able to convey to you something of its importance and its fascination. Then, in later Units (mainly Units 22 and 23), you will see how the same basic principles are applied to some of the processes involved in the chemistry of life.

THE CODEINE IS O.K. AND THE PHENOBARBITAL IS O.K., BUT THE FOOD AND DRUG ADMINISTRATION SAYS NO TO THE POWDERED BAT'S TOOTH."

2 CHARACTERISTICS OF CARBON COMPOUNDS

2.1 BONDING AND MOLECULAR STRUCTURE

Let us begin the study of the bonding and molecular structure of carbon compounds by looking at the simplest possible example. This is *methane*, the chief component of natural gas (Figure 4). First, we shall look at the bonding in methane.

Methane contains the elements carbon and hydrogen. Compounds that contain only the elements hydrogen and carbon are called **hydrocarbons**. Each molecule of methane contains one atom of carbon and four atoms of hydrogen. Chemists denote this in a shorthand form as CH_4. This is called the **molecular formula** of methane. It is important to realize that the molecular formula tells us only the numbers of each type of atom in the molecule, *not how the atoms are attached to each other*. The molecular formula of a substance is obtained by combining the results obtained from (i) analysing it to find out what elements it contains and (ii) measuring its molar mass (see Units 13–14).

☐ Carbon is in Group IV of the Periodic Table. Does the formula CH_4 fit in with your knowledge of the valencies of carbon and hydrogen?

■ Yes. Carbon has a valency of 4 and hydrogen has a valency of 1, so you would expect one carbon atom to combine with four hydrogen atoms.

FIGURE 4   A North Sea gas platform. North Sea gas consists predominantly of methane, CH_4.

CHEMICAL BONDING

STRUCTURAL FORMULA

NON-BONDING ELECTRON PAIRS

METHYL GROUP

ABBREVIATED STRUCTURAL FORMULA

From Units 13–14, you know that carbon invariably forms **bonds** by sharing electrons with other atoms rather than by forming ions. We can show this by drawing the *Lewis structure* of the molecule. Carbon has four electrons to share, so the Lewis structure of methane is as shown below. (Remember that the electrons in Lewis structures are denoted by different symbols simply to help with the book-keeping; there is no way in which individual electrons can be distinguished in a real molecule.)

methane

CH_4

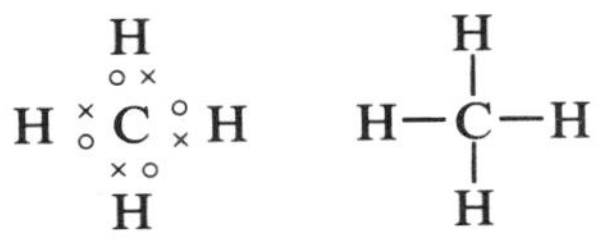

molecular formula   Lewis structure   structural formula

Each hydrogen atom has attained the electronic configuration of helium ($1s^2$) and the carbon atom has attained the electronic configuration of neon ($1s^2 2s^2 2p^6$). Writing out the bonding electrons in this way soon becomes tedious and inconvenient, so instead a shorthand representation is used in which each shared electron pair is denoted by a line; this is called the **structural formula**, as shown for methane. The line represents the covalent bond between each pair of atoms. Because carbon has four electrons to share, it always needs four others to complete the octet: that is, it always has a valency of 4. So any structural formula of a carbon compound that shows a carbon atom with more or less than four bonds is almost certainly wrong.

Carbon can form bonds with other elements, for example fluorine. Fluoromethane is a compound containing just the elements carbon, C, hydrogen, H, and fluorine, F: each molecule contains one atom of carbon, three atoms of hydrogen and one atom of fluorine.

☐ See if you can write down the molecular formula of fluoromethane.

■ The molecular formula for fluoromethane is CH_3F. You may wonder if H_3CF, H_3FC, etc. are equally acceptable. These are perfectly reasonable answers, but chemists have agreed the convention that molecular formulae of carbon compounds are always written in the order carbon, hydrogen, and then all other elements present in alphabetical order.

As fluorine is in Group VII, it needs only one more electron to attain the electronic configuration of neon. It can do this either by becoming an anion (as in, for example, sodium fluoride, Na^+F^-) or by sharing (as in hydrogen fluoride, H—F). The fluorine atom in fluoromethane attains the electronic configuration of neon by sharing electrons. So the Lewis structure and structural formula of fluoromethane are as shown below.

fluoromethane

CH_3F

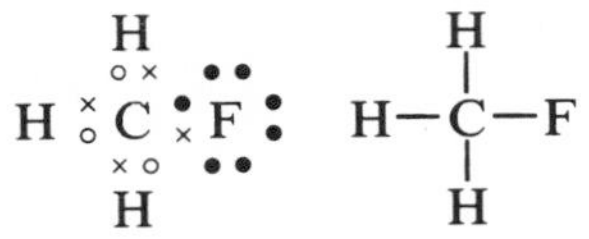

molecular formula   Lewis structure   structural formula

Note that fluorine only needs to form one covalent bond to obtain an outer octet of electrons: the other six electrons are already paired. These electrons form three unshared or **non-bonding electron pairs**. In the structural formula, the bonding electron pairs are denoted by lines, but the non-bonding electron pairs are usually not shown.

ITQ I   Bearing in mind the valencies of the elements nitrogen, N, oxygen, O, chlorine, Cl, and bromine, Br, which of these could, in principle, form

H
|
H—C—X   structural formula of
| compounds analogous
H   to fluoromethane

IV	V	VI	VII	0
				2 He
6 C	7 N	8 O	9 F	10 Ne
		16 S	17 Cl	18 Ar
			35 Br	36 Kr

FIGURE 5 The elements in the top right-hand portion of the Periodic Table.

compounds analogous to fluoromethane (that is, compounds with the structural formula shown in the margin, where X stands for N, O, Cl, Br)? (To help you, the relevant part of the Periodic Table is shown in Figure 5.)

You will probably remember from Units 13–14 that the elements fluorine, chlorine, bromine and iodine in Group VII of the Periodic Table have the same valency as hydrogen. We can use this knowledge to *predict* the existence of a whole range of compounds with molecular formulae containing one atom of carbon and four other atoms.

☐ Write down the molecular formula of such a compound containing C, H and F atoms only (other than fluoromethane).

■ There are two possibilities, CH_2F_2 and CHF_3.

Another example, this time without any hydrogen atoms, is CCl_2F_2, commonly known as Freon 12, which is used as the coolant in many refrigerators and freezers. We shall look at some of the uses of such compounds in Section 2.3.

Two other compounds containing a single carbon atom are *methanol* and *methylamine*. Methanol is manufactured on a vast scale for a variety of industrial uses. It is highly toxic—low doses cause blindness, larger amounts are fatal—and is mixed with ethanol (the alcohol in alcoholic drinks), along with other contaminants, to make the ethanol undrinkable, giving the mixture known as methylated spirits. Methylamine, which is manufactured from methanol, is also produced by stale fish and contributes to its characteristic unpleasant odour.

The formulae and Lewis structures of methanol and methylamine are shown below:

methanol

CH_4O

H   H
×○ ●● |
H ×○ C ×● O ○● H   H—C—O—H
×○ ●● |
H   H

molecular   Lewis   structural
formula   structure   formula

methylamine

CH_5N

H   H
○× ●● |
H ×○ C ×● N ○● H   H—C—N—H
×○ ●○ | |
H   H   H   H

molecular   Lewis   structural
formula   structure   formula

☐ Look at the Lewis structures of methanol and methylamine. What can you say about the electronic structures of each of the atoms in the two molecules?

■ They have attained a noble gas structure by sharing electrons. This is the basis of the statement that hydrogen has a valency of 1, oxygen a valency of 2, nitrogen a valency of 3 and carbon a valency of 4.

☐ Look at the structural formulae of the four compounds methane, fluoromethane, methanol and methylamine. What feature do they have in common?

■ All four compounds contain the same group, shown in the margin.

H
|
H—C—
|
H
the methyl group

This group is called the **methyl group** and its structure is usually abbreviated to CH_3— or —CH_3. Both representations means the same thing: a carbon atom, to which are bonded three hydrogen atoms, and one electron pair shared with some other atom. We can abbreviate the structures of other groups similarly. So, we can write simplified structural formulae (known as **abbreviated structural formulae**) for fluoromethane, methanol and methylamine as CH_3—F, CH_3—OH, and CH_3—NH_2 respectively.

HYDROCARBON GROUP

FUNCTIONAL GROUP

INTERMOLECULAR FORCES

LONDON FORCES

ELECTRIC DIPOLE

RELATIVE MOLECULAR MASS

The methyl group is an example of a **hydrocarbon group** and the $-F$, $-OH$ and $-NH_2$ groups are examples of a **functional group**. Chemists group the atoms in this particular way because it conveniently separates the active part from the inactive: in the majority of reactions, *it is the functional group* (here, $-F$, $-OH$ or $-NH_2$) *that is reactive and is changed in some way, while the hydrocarbon group* (here, the CH_3- group) *persists unchanged*. In Section 6, you will see how this division of a molecule into an active part and an inactive part helps enormously in making sense of the many types of reactions that carbon compounds can undergo.

For convenience and clarity, from now on we shall mainly use abbreviated structural formulae. They convey most of the essential information about the molecule, but avoid what for larger molecules become very cumbersome full structural formulae. However, you should always be aware of the presence of any bonds not shown and of non-bonding electron pairs on atoms such as N, O, F, Cl, Br and I. Also, you will find it useful when drawing or checking structural formulae to remember that carbon has a valency of 4 (and so will form four covalent bonds), nitrogen a valency of 3, oxygen a valency of 2, and that hydrogen, fluorine, chlorine, bromine and iodine each have a valency of 1 (Table 1). If you remember this, you will be able to draw the correct number of bonds for each atom: any formula which does not conform to the valencies shown is almost certainly wrong.

TABLE 1   Valencies of some common elements found in carbon compounds

Element	Symbol	Valency
hydrogen	H	1
carbon	C	4
nitrogen	N	3
oxygen	O	2
fluorine	F	1
chlorine	Cl	1
bromine	Br	1
iodine	I	1

SAQ 1   Without referring back, write down the Lewis structures of methane, CH_4, and methanol, CH_3-OH.

SAQ 2   Write down: (a) the Lewis structure of the compound fluoro-methylamine, $F-CH_2-NH_2$; and (b) its (full) structural formula.

SAQ 3   Which of the following abbreviated structural formulae have Lewis structures in which one or more of the atoms does *not* have a noble gas configuration?

(a) CH_3-O-Cl (c) $I-CH-Br$

(b) CH_3-NH_2-F (d) $Cl-CH_2-OH$

2.2 MOLECULAR STRUCTURE AND PHYSICAL PROPERTIES

Before going on to consider the chemical properties of carbon compounds, let us look at some of the physical characteristics of the four compounds we have discussed so far: methane, fluoromethane, methanol and methylamine. You may be surprised to learn that the molecular structure and the physical state of a covalent substance are intimately related.

You saw in Unit 16 that whether a substance is a solid, a liquid or a gas is determined by the balance between the average kinetic energy of the molecules (which is proportional to the absolute temperature of the substance) and the energy due to the cohesive forces between the molecules. As we shall see shortly, the cohesive forces between molecules can arise in a number of ways.

Pure solids do not change gradually into liquids over a range of temperatures, but do so at one particular temperature, the melting temperature. Similarly, liquids change into gases at a particular temperature, the boiling temperature. For example, ice melts at $0\,°C$ and pure water boils at $100\,°C$ at normal atmospheric pressure. The melting and boiling temperatures of the four carbon compounds we have already discussed are given in Table 2.

TABLE 2 Melting and boiling temperatures of methane and some of its derivatives

Compound	Formula	Melting temperature/°C	Boiling temperature/°C
methane	CH_4	-182	-162
fluoromethane	CH_3-F	-142	-78
methanol	CH_3-OH	-94	$+65$
methylamine	CH_3-NH_2	-93	-6

It is very difficult to predict or explain the absolute melting or boiling temperature of a substance. It is much easier, though, to account for the *relative* values in a series of compounds. This is particularly true of boiling temperatures and we shall concentrate on these. First, we need to ask what is the nature of the cohesive forces that bind one molecule to another.

There are three main types of these **intermolecular forces**: London forces, dipole–dipole forces, and hydrogen bonds. As you will see, all of these are primarily electrostatic in nature and result from the net attraction between the electrons of one molecule and the nuclei of another.

☐ In which of the compounds in Table 2 do you think the cohesive forces between the molecules are greatest?

■ The boiling temperature of methanol is much higher than that of the others, suggesting that the forces between the molecules of methanol are stronger than those between the other molecules. We shall see why in a moment.

Consider the series of halogen molecules that you met in Units 13–14: fluorine, F_2, chlorine, Cl_2, bromine, Br_2, and iodine, I_2. You may recall that the first two are gases at normal temperatures, bromine is a liquid and iodine is a solid. But if cooled to a sufficiently low temperature, chlorine and fluorine would liquefy and (eventually) solidify. So, clearly, there are attractive forces between the molecules for all four elements. What, then, is the nature of these forces? It turns out that they are electrical in origin, even though these four molecules are electrically neutral and both atoms making up each molecule have an equal share of the bonding electrons. These forces, called **London forces***, arise in the following way.

On average, the electrons in each molecule are evenly distributed about the molecular axis: we can say that the centre of negative charge (due to the electrons) coincides with the centre of positive charge (due to the protons in the nuclei). However, because the electrons are constantly in motion, *at any instant* their distribution is not uniform (Figure 6: overleaf), resulting in a momentary separation of the centres of positive and negative charge. Such a separation of positive and negative charge is called an **electric dipole**. These transient dipoles give rise to short-range attractive forces between the molecules. (You will recall from Unit 9 that there is an attractive force between electrical charges of opposite sign.) It turns out that the magnitude of the London forces depends on the **relative molecular mass** of a molecule. The relative molecular mass, M_r, of a compound is defined as the ratio of the mass of one molecule of that compound to the mass of one atom of ^{12}C, and consequently has no units. It has the same numerical value as the molar mass (Units 13–14).

---

* Named after the German physicist, Fritz London, who first drew attention to them in 1930. You may find that the term 'van der Waals forces' is used by some authors instead of 'London forces'.

DIPOLE–DIPOLE FORCES

HYDROGEN BONDS

HALOCARBON

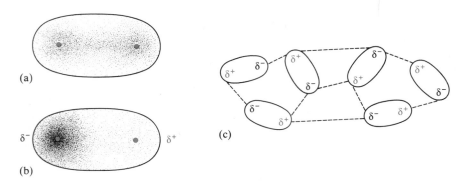

(a)

(b)

(c)

FIGURE 6   The origin of London forces: (a) shows a molecule made up of two atoms with the electrons (denoted by the shading) distributed evenly around the two positive nuclei; (b) shows how the electrons can transiently be distributed unevenly. Though *on average* the distribution of charge is even, the molecule can none the less have a very temporary dipole, that is, can be slightly positive at one end and slightly negative at the other. The transient dipole in one molecule can then be attracted by the transient dipole in an adjacent molecule, (c). The result is a net attractive force between the molecules (dashed lines).

The higher the relative molecular mass, the greater the attraction between molecules due to London forces.

☐ Does this explain the sequence of boiling temperatures in the halogen series: F_2, $-188\,°C$; Cl_2, $-35\,°C$; Br_2, $59\,°C$; I_2, $184\,°C$?

■ Yes. The sequence of boiling temperatures parallels the progressive increase in relative molecular mass.

London forces operate between all molecules (and even between the atoms of the noble gases). But for some molecules there are additional attractive forces. Hydrogen chloride, HCl, has a relative molecular mass of 36.5, and fluorine, F_2, has a relative molecular mass of 38. If London forces alone were operating, these two molecules might be expected to have rather similar boiling temperatures. In fact, hydrogen chloride boils at $-85\,°C$, whereas fluorine, as we have seen, boils at $-188\,°C$. This is because *additional* electrical forces operate between hydrogen chloride molecules.

As you saw in Units 13–14, the two atoms in hydrogen chloride have different electronegativities and so do not have an equal share of the bonding electrons. The hydrogen atom has a partial positive charge and the chlorine a partial negative charge. So each molecule of hydrogen chloride has a *permanent* electric dipole, in addition to the *transient* dipoles that give rise to the London forces, and these permanent dipoles also attract one another (Figure 7). These additional forces, called **dipole–dipole forces**, are responsible for the boiling temperature of hydrogen chloride being higher than would be expected from consideration of London forces alone. (For much larger molecules, in which there might be just one polar bond among many that are not, the boiling temperature would be little higher than expected by consideration of London forces alone.)

FIGURE 7   Cohesive forces between the permanent dipoles in polar covalent molecules, for example hydrogen chloride. The $\delta+$ and $\delta-$ signs signify partial positive and negative charges. The dashed lines signify attractive forces.

Carbon and hydrogen have roughly equal electronegativities, whereas fluorine is much more electronegative than the other two. By considering the forces that you expect to operate between (a) methane molecules and (b) fluoromethane molecules, predict which is likely to have the higher boiling temperature.

Because the electronegativities of carbon and hydrogen are similar, you would expect there to be no permanent dipole in methane, so the only forces acting are the London forces. By contrast, the C—F bond in fluoromethane is polar, so, in addition, there will be dipole–dipole forces between fluoromethane molecules. Also the relative molecular mass of fluoromethane (34) is larger than that of methane (16), so the London forces will be larger in the former. On both counts, the boiling temperature of fluoromethane would be expected to be higher than that of methane, which is confirmed by the values given in Table 2.

Fluoromethane CH_3—F, methanol, CH_3—OH, and methylamine, CH_3—NH_2, have roughly equal relative molecular masses, yet the boiling temperatures (Table 2) are very different. Is it possible to account for these differences on the basis of the above two types of force? (Fluorine has a higher electronegativity than oxygen, which in turn has a higher value than nitrogen.)

The answer is no. The London forces should be very similar, and if anything the dipole–dipole forces should decrease across the series CH_3—F, CH_3—OH, CH_3—NH_2. This suggests that the boiling temperatures should decrease, yet the value for methanol is much higher than that for CH_3—F or CH_3—NH_2. The explanation involves an additional, extremely important, intermolecular force. Molecules that contain hydrogen atoms attached to oxygen (or to a lesser extent nitrogen) have a special ability to form weak extra bonds: these are called **hydrogen bonds**. They are called 'bonds' because they are directional and stronger than the London or dipole–dipole forces; however they are considerably weaker than the covalent bonds between atoms within molecules. But as you will see in Units 22 to 24, hydrogen bonds play a crucial role in the chemistry of life.

Hydrogen bonds can best be thought of as a special case of dipole–dipole forces. They arise because hydrogen atoms are so much smaller than other atoms: this allows the positive end of the O—H dipole to approach more closely the negative end of another O—H dipole, and leads to particularly strong attractive forces (Figure 8).

Hydrogen bonds between —NH_2 groups are generally weaker than those between —OH groups. So we would expect the effect to be less marked for methylamine, CH_3—NH_2, than for methanol, CH_3—OH. This expectation is borne out by the data in Table 2: methylamine boils at $-6\,°C$ and methanol at $65\,°C$. This contrasts with fluoromethane, which cannot form hydrogen bonds with other fluoromethane molecules, and which boils at $-78\,°C$.

These explanations are only qualitative; that is, they do not allow us to predict the numerical values of boiling temperatures. None the less, these simple ideas often enable chemists to predict with considerable confidence whether a given compound will be a solid, a liquid or a gas at normal temperatures and pressures, provided they have this information for other related compounds. Further, as you will see in Section 3.2, these same ideas allow us to explain trends in the solubilities of carbon compounds, that is, the ability of one compound to dissolve in another.

SAQ 4 The element bromine, Br_2 (relative molecular mass 160), boils at $59\,°C$, whereas the compound iodine monochloride, ICl (relative molecular mass 162.5), boils at $97\,°C$. Is this order of boiling temperatures consistent with the arguments presented in Section 2.2? If so, which of the three main types of intermolecular force predominates?

SAQ 5 The boiling temperatures of the hydrides of the elements in Group VI of the Periodic Table are as follows: H_2O, $100\,°C$; H_2S, $-61\,°C$; H_2Se, $-42\,°C$; H_2Te, $-2\,°C$. Explain: (a) the trend in boiling temperatures on going down the Group from H_2S to H_2Te; and (b) the anomalously high value for H_2O.

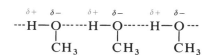

FIGURE 8 Hydrogen bonding between methanol molecules. The dashed lines signify attractive forces. These are stronger for hydrogen bonding than for dipole–dipole forces because the small size of the hydrogen atom allows it to approach the oxygen atom closely.

2.3 HALOCARBONS AT LARGE

The relationship between the molecular structure of a substance and its boiling temperature may seem to you to be somewhat academic. But the principles that we have been discussing have a very practical application in the family of substances known as **halocarbons**, some of which are used as refrigerants in freezers, refrigerators and air-conditioning units. The term halocarbon is used for compounds with molecules that contain carbon and one or more halogens (Group VII elements), with or without hydrogen, and

OZONE LAYER

no other elements. The halocarbons used as refrigerants always contain fluorine atoms. These compounds are often known as Freons, after the trade name used by the chemical company (du Pont) that first developed them.

Although the principle of mechanical refrigeration has been known since the early 19th century, its widespread application was limited largely to industry until the 1920s. It was then that the breakthrough came with the discovery of a refrigerant suitable for both domestic and commercial applications.

Many substances that are gases at normal temperatures (though not all) can be liquefied simply by compression; that is, by increasing the pressure. The canisters of butane you used for the experiments in Units 13–14 provide a good example. When such a substance is liquefied by compression, heat is given out. When the pressure is reduced and the liquid becomes a gas again, the same amount of energy must be absorbed from the surroundings, thereby causing a drop in temperature. This is the principle of refrigeration.

In a refrigerator, the heat liberated on liquefaction by compression of the gaseous refrigerant is dissipated through an external radiator (see Figure 9). The liquid then passes through an expansion valve; the pressure is thereby reduced and the liquid vaporizes. Heat is absorbed from the interior of the refrigerator, which is thereby cooled. The refrigerant is then recycled.

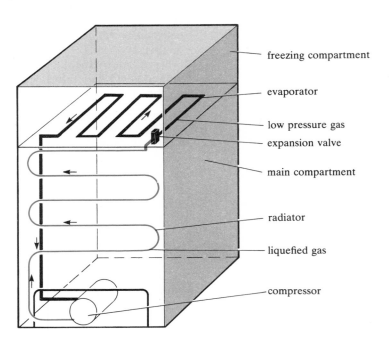

freezing compartment

evaporator

low pressure gas

expansion valve

main compartment

radiator

liquefied gas

compressor

FIGURE 9 A schematic representation of the compression–cooling cycle in a domestic refrigerator.

Until the 1920s, the refrigerant industry depended on the use of compounds such as ammonia, NH_3, sulphur dioxide, SO_2, and chloromethane, CH_3Cl, as refrigerants. Unfortunately, these substances are corrosive, toxic and/or highly inflammable. The trend towards domestic and commercial use of refrigeration in the USA during the 1920s stimulated a search for a safer refrigerant.

Ideally, a refrigerant should be non-toxic, non-flammable, non-corrosive, chemically stable and have a boiling temperature between $0\,°C$ and $-40\,°C$. Inspired guesswork led Thomas Midgeley, who discovered the first suitable substance, to focus on fluorine compounds. Evidently no one had previously considered that, although many fluorine compounds are exceedingly toxic and reactive, some might be non-toxic and unreactive. Midgeley chose dichlorofluoromethane*, $CHCl_2F$, as his initial target, and, on testing

* A compound name such as this is pronounced by splitting up the word into its constituent parts: 'di-chloro-fluoro-methane'.

the substance, found it to be completely non-toxic, as well as being non-flammable and non-corrosive. Although $CHCl_2F$ itself turned out to have too high a boiling temperature (9 °C) for use as a refrigerant, from this discovery sprang a huge industry devoted to the production of such halocarbons.

By varying the atoms involved, suitable compounds with a variety of boiling temperatures are now available, and which is the most appropriate depends on the particular application. The most widely used halocarbons are listed in Table 3, together with some of their uses. The most commonly used refrigerant in ordinary domestic refrigerators is CCl_2F_2. However, the boiling temperature of -30 °C is too high for use in deep-freezes and $CHClF_2$ is more frequently used for these.

TABLE 3   Some widely used halocarbons

Molecular formula	Common name	Boiling temperature/°C	Uses
CCl_3F	Freon 11	24	refrigerant, aerosol propellant, blowing agent for foam plastics
$CBrClF_2$	BCF	-4	fire-extinguishing agent*
CCl_2F_2	Freon 12	-30	refrigerant, aerosol propellant, blowing agent for foam plastics
$CHClF_2$	Freon 22	-41	refrigerant

* The halocarbons in this Table are examples of the very few carbon compounds that do not burn.

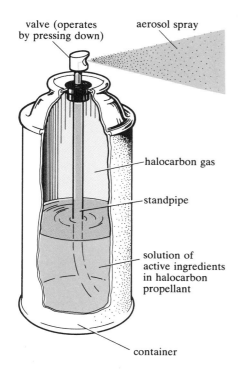

valve (operates by pressing down)

aerosol spray

halocarbon gas

standpipe

solution of active ingredients in halocarbon propellant

container

FIGURE 10   Cut-away view of a typical aerosol spray can.

Another use for these compounds, which has mushroomed since the Second World War, is their use as aerosol propellants for a vast range of products, from hair-styling mousse to paint, from insecticides to polishes (Figure 10). They are also used as 'blowing agents' for making foam plastics.

Halocarbons containing bromine are used in fire-extinguishing systems fitted in museums, libraries, art galleries, telephone exchanges and computer installations: they are also used to combat aircraft fires and in the portable extinguishers carried in motor vehicles, both public and private. These compounds are expensive, but the cost is justified in the above situations by their great efficiency: they quench a fire in a matter of seconds by interfering with the burning process at the molecular level. Plate 4 shows a typical portable aerosol extinguisher, containing 'BCF' (**b**romo**c**hloro-di**f**luoromethane, $CBrClF_2$), for use in cars.

Halocarbons owe much of their usefulness to the fact that they are unreactive substances. Unfortunately, this very property means that, as the halocarbons are released into the atmosphere, they constitute a long-term environmental hazard. Some of the halocarbons, particularly Freon 11, CCl_3F, and Freon 12, CCl_2F_2, are so unreactive that they are able to diffuse up into the stratosphere. The stratosphere is the region of the Earth's atmosphere that extends from a height of about 8 km above the Poles (16 km above the Equator) to around 90 km. There the action of the Sun's ultraviolet rays splits the molecules into reactive fragments that destroy ozone molecules, O_3, in the stratosphere (Figure 11). The ozone in the stratosphere (the so-called **ozone layer**) plays a vital role in shielding the Earth's surface from the Sun's harmful ultraviolet radiation by absorbing radiation with wavelengths between about 200 and 300 nm. One of the main concerns is that an increase in the amount of ultraviolet radiation reaching the Earth's surface will give rise to an increase in skin cancer. For example, one estimate is that a 1% reduction in the ozone concentration would lead to a 6% increase in the incidence of skin cancer.

It was Mario Molina and F. Sherwood Rowland, two chemists at the University of California, who suggested in 1974 that the increasing quantities of halocarbons in the atmosphere pose a long-term threat to the atmospheric ozone layer. You may think that the problem is a minor one, but the

FIGURE 11 Halocarbons used to make foam plastic such as expanded polystyrene, in fire extinguishers, as the propellant in spray cans, as the coolant in air conditioners, refrigerators and freezers, and to clean computing equipment, diffuse up into the stratosphere where they can attack the Earth's protective ozone layer (shown in the Figure as a pink band).

annual production of the halocarbons concerned is 8×10^5 tonnes (1986 figure) and, in 1984 alone, *seven billion* (7×10^9) aerosol cans were manufactured. According to present estimates (1986), current rates of production will cause a depletion of 9% of the atmospheric ozone within 70 years. Because of their unreactivity, even if all production stopped and no more was released into the atmosphere, it would take many decades for the ozone concentration to return to normal.

Over the past decade or more, there has been a great deal of controversy over the accuracy of these predictions because of the difficulty of measuring a long-term depletion of a few per cent, given the natural variation in ozone levels. However, each year since 1979, an increasingly substantial depletion, dubbed an 'ozone hole' by the press, has been detected in the total amount of ozone over the Antarctic. The 'ozone hole', which represents a much larger depletion than predicted, begins to form during late August, is greatest in early October, and then begins to weaken, with the ozone returning to more normal levels by mid-November. The effect has grown year by year, such that by 1986 the maximum depletion amounted to 40% of the corresponding 1979 levels, that is, 163 Dobson units as compared to 270 Dobson units (Plate 5).*

Many countries have for some years been calling for severe restrictions on the further production of these halocarbons, though until late 1987 the United Kingdom had been among the most reluctant to impose such restraints. However, the increasingly firm evidence that the Antarctic 'ozone hole' is due to the halocarbons in the atmosphere has convinced even the most sceptical of the need for urgent action. As a result, the 24 nations attending a conference held in September 1987 (under the auspices of the United Nations Environment Programme) to discuss the problem agreed to a 50% cut in production by 1999. However, this agreement still has to be ratified by the individual countries concerned. Meanwhile, at the time of writing (late 1987), although the use of halocarbons in sprays, for example, has decreased substantially since 1980, their use in the production of foam plastics and as solvents has markedly increased.

* The total amount of ozone in a vertical column through which the Sun's rays have to penetrate is traditionally measured in 'Dobson units'. The unit is named after the geophysicist who pioneered the method of measuring ozone levels that is still in use today.

"OH, FOR PETE'S SAKE, LET'S JUST GET SOME OZONE AND SEND IT BACK UP THERE!"

SUMMARY OF SECTION 2

Modern life has been transformed by the investigation and exploitation of the chemical and physical properties of carbon compounds. Examples are legion: the use of pesticides in food production, hydrocarbon fuels for food transport, refrigerants for food preservation, and plastics for food packaging, illustrates this dependence in just one area. Further, the existence of life as we know it is based on the chemistry of carbon compounds.

Attention was focused first on four of the simplest carbon compounds, those containing just one carbon atom: methane, CH_4, fluoromethane, CH_3-F, methanol, CH_3-OH, and methylamine, CH_3-NH_2. The molecular formula, Lewis structure and structural formula of each of these four compounds were examined in turn. The observations that each of these molecules (with the exception of methane) is made up of a reactive functional group and an inactive hydrocarbon group is encapsulated in the use of abbreviated structural formulae.

By considering the three main types of intermolecular force (London forces, dipole–dipole forces and hydrogen bonds), it proved possible to account for the trend in boiling temperatures of methane, fluoromethane, methanol and methylamine. London forces are present for all molecules. Molecules with polar bonds (e.g. fluoromethane) also have an additional intermolecular attraction due to dipole–dipole forces. Molecules with $-OH$ groups (and to a lesser extent $-NH_2$ groups) have a third type of attraction due to the presence of hydrogen bonds. In general, the stronger the cohesive forces between the molecules, the higher the boiling temperature.

The use of these and other simple ideas led to the discovery of the Freons, the first safe refrigerants. The properties of these halocarbons have given rise to their use on a large scale not only as refrigerants but also as aerosol propellants, fire-extinguishing agents and foam-blowing agents. The indiscriminate release of these substances is widely believed to have given rise to a major environmental hazard: depletion of the stratospheric ozone layer.

SAQ 6 Which of the following statements are true and which are false? (Try to answer without referring back.)

(a) Hydrogen bonds between amino groups ($-NH_2$) are generally stronger than those between hydroxyl groups ($-OH$).
(b) London forces exist between all molecules.
(c) There is no functional group in methane, CH_4.
(d) The molecular formula of methanol is CH_3-OH.
(e) Chloromethane, CH_3-Cl, is a halocarbon.

SAQ 7 Bromomethane, CH_3Br (relative molecular mass 95), boils at $4\,°C$ and iodomethane, CH_3I (relative molecular mass 142), boils at $42\,°C$. Given that iodine has a lower electronegativity than bromine (and therefore the $C-I$ bond is less polar then the $C-Br$ bond), account for the fact that CH_3I boils at a higher temperature than CH_3Br, in terms of the three types of intermolecular forces described in Section 2.2.

3 FAMILIES OF COMPOUNDS— CATENATION

In this Section we shall begin to look at why there are so many carbon compounds. We shall see that each of the four compounds studied in Section 2 is just the first member of a whole series of such compounds, made possible by carbon's ability to form long chains of atoms. After a brief look at how the physical properties of these compounds vary within a series, we shall go on to see how, for a given molecular formula, the atoms can often be arranged in a number of ways to give a rich variety of molecular structures.

3.1 HOMOLOGOUS SERIES

In the previous Section, your study of carbon compounds was limited to those containing just one carbon atom. So far you have had no reason to regard carbon as anything but an ordinary element. But the enormous importance of the chemistry of carbon compounds derives from a property shared by no other element to anything like the same extent. Carbon is unique because it can use its four valencies to form bonds with itself apparently without limit. This property is called **catenation** (from the Latin, *catena*, meaning 'chain'). It is the ability of carbon to catenate that gives rise to the great number and variety of carbon compounds.

As before, we shall begin with the simplest compounds, in this case those in which the carbon atoms are connected in a linear chain, like beads in a necklace. First, let us look at the hydrocarbons, compounds that contain just carbon and hydrogen. You have already met the simplest such compound, methane, CH_4.

> Remembering that carbon has a valency of 4 and hydrogen a valency of 1, write down the structural formula of the compound with *two* carbon atoms linked together and using the remaining valencies to form bonds to hydrogen atoms.

The hydrocarbon with two carbon atoms is called ethane; each carbon atom uses one of its valencies for the $C-C$ bond, leaving a total of six remaining for hydrogen atoms. Carrying this process one stage further gives the compound called propane, with three carbon atoms and eight hydrogen atoms. The next member of the series, with four carbon atoms and ten hydrogens, is called butane.

ethane   propane   butane

Because of carbon's ability to form chains apparently without limit, we could carry this process on to 100, 200, or even 1 000 carbon atoms, with the near-certain knowledge that, even if that compound does not already exist, *it could in principle be made*. The names and formulae of the first ten members of this series, known as the linear **alkanes**, are listed in Table 4. These compounds are found (along with many others) in natural gas and petroleum*.

TABLE 4   The first ten members of the series of linear alkanes

Name	Molecular formula	Abbreviated structural formula*
methane	CH_4	CH_4
ethane	C_2H_6	CH_3-CH_3
propane	C_3H_8	$CH_3-CH_2-CH_3$
butane	C_4H_{10}	$CH_3-CH_2-CH_2-CH_3$
pentane	C_5H_{12}	$CH_3-CH_2-CH_2-CH_2-CH_3$
hexane	C_6H_{14}	$CH_3-CH_2-CH_2-CH_2-CH_2-CH_3$
heptane	C_7H_{16}	$CH_3-CH_2-CH_2-CH_2-CH_2-CH_2-CH_3$
octane	C_8H_{18}	$CH_3-CH_2-CH_2-CH_2-CH_2-CH_2-CH_2-CH_3$
nonane	C_9H_{20}	$CH_3-CH_2-CH_2-CH_2-CH_2-CH_2-CH_2-CH_2-CH_3$
decane	$C_{10}H_{22}$	$CH_3-CH_2-CH_2-CH_2-CH_2-CH_2-CH_2-CH_2-CH_2-CH_3$

* For the larger molecules, writing even the abbreviated structural formula becomes unwieldy. So chemists often abbreviate even more and write decane, for example, as $CH_3-(CH_2)_8-CH_3$.

What is the difference between the structural formulae of (a) propane and butane and (b) nonane and decane (Table 4)?

In each case they differ by one $-CH_2-$ group. Such a group of compounds, in which the structural formulae differ only by an integral number of $-CH_2-$ groups, is called a **homologous series**.

Just as the homologous series of alkanes shown in Table 4 has methane as its first member, so there are homologous series with the other compounds that you met in Section 2 as the first member: fluoromethane, CH_3F, methanol, CH_3-OH, and methylamine, CH_3-NH_2. The series based on fluoromethane is called the fluoroalkanes and the first few members are listed in Table 5.

TABLE 5   The first six members of the series of linear fluoroalkanes

Name	Abbreviated structural formula
fluoromethane	CH_3-F
fluoroethane	CH_3-CH_2-F
1-fluoropropane	$CH_3-CH_2-CH_2-F$
1-fluorobutane	$CH_3-CH_2-CH_2-CH_2-F$
1-fluoropentane	$CH_3-CH_2-CH_2-CH_2-CH_2-F$
1-fluorohexane	$CH_3-CH_2-CH_2-CH_2-CH_2-CH_2-F$

By now, you may be wondering whether or not there is any systematic way in which carbon compounds are named, and also whether or not you are expected to remember the names of individual compounds. The answer to the first question is, fortunately, yes; the answer to the second is most certainly no!

* The trace in the front cover illustration shows an analysis of crude oil using the technique of gas chromatography that you will see used in the TV programme 'Organic molecules in action'. Each major peak corresponds to a member of the series of linear alkanes.

HYDROXYL GROUP

AMINO GROUP

ALKANOL

ALCOHOL

ALKYL GROUP

ALKANAMINE

ALKYLAMINE

In writing Units 17–18, we have deliberately limited the number of new chemical names and terms in order to encourage you to focus attention on the concepts rather than the nomenclature. However, one cannot get much further without grasping the nettle of terminology, if for no other reason than that it is necessary for the communication of chemical facts and ideas. So from now on, whenever we introduce a new type of compound, you will also be shown how such compounds are named. However, you will *not* be asked to answer questions in an assignment or in the examination that require you to remember any individual names.

The systematic nomenclature developed for organic compounds reflects their chemical characteristics. A typical organic compound containing carbon, hydrogen, oxygen and/or nitrogen tends to react in such a way that the carbon framework is preserved; that is, its reactions usually involve the functional groups. Thus, in naming such a compound, attention is nearly always focused *initially* on the carbon framework, *then* on the functional group. The stem of the name is derived from the name of the corresponding hydrocarbon (Table 4).

Let us see how that works for the fluoroalkanes. The first member of the series is called fluoromethane: this is derived by attaching the prefix *fluoro-* to the name of the corresponding hydrocarbon, in this case methane. Indeed, this is how the name *fluoro*alkane is derived from the name alkane.

☐ Using this rule, what is the name of the fluoro- compound corresponding to nonane?

■ Fluorononane.

There is one slight additional complication. As you will see in Section 3.3, for chains of three carbons or more, there is more than one point of attachment possible for a functional group. That is why four of the fluoroalkanes listed in Table 5 have the numeral '1' included in the name: this indicates that the fluorine atom is attached to the first carbon atom. So the fluoroalkane corresponding to nonane with the fluorine atom at the end of the chain would be 1-fluorononane.

The other two functional groups that you have already come across, in addition to the fluorine atom (—F), are the **hydroxyl group** (—OH) and the **amino group** (—NH$_2$). The homologous series based on methanol is called the **alkanols**; the first few members are shown in Table 6.

TABLE 6   The first six members of the series of linear alkanols (alcohols)

Systematic name	Abbreviated structural formula	Older* name
methanol	$CH_3—OH$	methyl alcohol
ethanol	$CH_3—CH_2—OH$	ethyl alcohol
propan-1-ol	$CH_3—CH_2—CH_2—OH$	*n*-propyl alcohol
butan-1-ol	$CH_3—CH_2—CH_2—CH_2—OH$	*n*-butyl alcohol
pentan-1-ol	$CH_3—CH_2—CH_2—CH_2—CH_2—OH$	*n*-pentyl alcohol
hexan-1-ol	$CH_3—CH_2—CH_2—CH_2—CH_2—CH_2—OH$	*n*-hexyl alcohol

* The prefix '*n*' (standing for normal) simply indicates that the hydrocarbon group is linear; it corresponds to the '1' in the systematic name.

The compounds are named by replacing the final -e in the corresponding hydrocarbon by -ol. For example, the name methan*ol* is so derived from methan*e*, and indeed this is how the name alkan*ol* is derived from alkan*e*.

☐ Using this rule, what is the name of the alkanol corresponding to the hydrocarbon octane?

■ Octanol.

As with the fluoroalkanes, for chains of three carbons or more, there is more than one point of attachment possible for the functional group. That is why four of the alkanols listed in Table 6 have the numeral '1' included in the name: this indicates that the —OH group is attached to the first carbon atom. So the correct name for the linear alkanol with eight carbons and the hydroxyl group at the end of the carbon chain would be octan-1-ol.

You may have come across another way of naming alkanols, in which the name of the series is the **alcohols**; the individual members then have two-part names with the first part being the name of the hydrocarbon group and the second part being the word alcohol (Table 6). The hydrocarbon group is named by replacing the final -ane in the corresponding hydrocarbon by the suffix -yl. Thus, the general name of such a hydrocarbon group is an **alkyl group** (from alk*ane*).

☐ What is the alternative name for ethanol using this system?

■ Ethyl alcohol (eth*yl* derived from eth*ane*).

Table 7 shows the first few members of the homologous series of **alkanamines**, compounds with the amino (—NH_2) functional group. The older name for the alkanamines is **alkylamines**.

TABLE 7   The first six members of the series of linear alkanamines (alkylamines)

Systematic name	Abbreviated structural formula	Older name
methanamine	CH_3—NH_2	methylamine
ethanamine	CH_3—CH_2—NH_2	ethylamine
propan-1-amine	CH_3—CH_2—CH_2—NH_2	*n*-propylamine
butan-1-amine	CH_3—CH_2—CH_2—CH_2—NH_2	*n*-butylamine
pentan-1-amine	CH_3—CH_2—CH_2—CH_2—CH_2—NH_2	*n*-pentylamine
hexan-1-amine	CH_3—CH_2—CH_2—CH_2—CH_2—CH_2—NH_2	*n*-hexylamine

Alkanamines are named in an analogous way to alkanols: the final -e of the corresponding hydrocarbon name is replaced by -amine.

☐ Using this rule, what is the name of the alkanamine corresponding to decane?

■ Decan-1-amine. Remember that for chains of three carbon atoms or more you need to specify the number of the carbon atom to which the functional group is attached.

As with alkanols, there is another method of naming amines where the name of the corresponding alkyl group is used. For example, ethanamine would be called ethylamine using this system; note that ethylamine is one word whereas ethyl alcohol is two.

These latter two homologous series (the alkanols/alcohols and the alkanamines/alkylamines) illustrate a common problem in naming carbon compounds. Most well-known carbon compounds have at least two names, one of which is usually historical in origin, and the other derived from an internationally agreed system of nomenclature. The use of the latter is clearly essential if every organic substance is to have a completely descriptive name which corresponds to a unique structural formula. Names that are not in any sense descriptive should be avoided as far as possible, but this is not always practicable. Quite obviously, the systematic name all-*trans*-9-(2,6,6-trimethylcyclohex-1-enyl)-3,7-dimethylnona-2,4,6,8-tetraen-1-ol is not a very handy name for vitamin A! Chemists tend to prefer the more systematic names, though not with complete consistency: while the systematic names for the individual alkanols (alcohols) have been widely adopted, the series is most commonly known as the alcohols! In the case of the alkanamines (alkylamines), the older names are more commonly used. (You may have noticed this in Section 2, where methanol was used not methyl alcohol, but methylamine not methanamine.) You will find that the older, less systematic, names are particularly common in biochemistry (Unit 22). In these

Units, we shall follow general practice and call the two series of compounds alcohols and alkylamines; for the individual alcohols we shall use the more systematic names, while using the older names for individual alkylamines.

Since you are not expected to learn these names, to help you, the chemical names used in these Units are listed in Appendix II and cross-referenced to the alternative name where there is one. For example, if you look up hexan-1-amine it will tell you that it is the systematic name for *n*-hexylamine, and vice versa. Also, where appropriate, there is a short description, *for interest only*, of a compound's use and/or occurrence. For example, ethanol is described as the alcohol in alcoholic beverages, and butane as a portable fuel used in (for example) camping stoves.

You might begin to wonder how chemists are able to cope with such variety. Fortunately, as we have already hinted, it is possible to discern patterns. Just as the elements are collected into families (the Groups of the Periodic Table), so there are families of carbon compounds that share common features. They are collected together because, though each is an individual compound, they have similar chemical properties. The alkanes burn, and if heated they undergo a series of complex reactions that are of great importance industrially. But as far as most organic chemists are concerned, the alkanes are unreactive. This is the basis for the distinction made in Section 2.1 between a functional group and a hydrocarbon group, because in most reactions the hydrocarbon group persists unchanged.

You will be studying the chemical properties of different types of compound in Section 6, when the usefulness of the concept of a functional group and a hydrocarbon group will become more apparent. But for the moment we shall concentrate on the *physical* properties of a homologous series of compounds.

SAQ 8 Select pairs of compounds from the list 1–8 that are members of the same homologous series.

1 $CH_3{-}CH_2{-}CH_2{-}OH$ 5 $F{-}CH_2{-}CH_2{-}OH$

2 $CH_3{-}CH_2{-}NH_2$ 6 $HO{-}CH_2{-}CH_2{-}OH$

3 $CH_3{-}OH$ 7 $CH_3{-}CH_2{-}CH_2{-}CH_2{-}NH_2$

4 $NH_2{-}CH_2{-}CH_2{-}OH$ 8 $F{-}CH_2{-}CH_2{-}CH_2{-}OH$

3.2 PHYSICAL PROPERTIES OF HOMOLOGOUS SERIES

Figure 12 shows the boiling temperatures of the linear alkanes listed in Table 4 (p. 19) and of the corresponding alcohols, plotted against the number of carbon atoms in the chain.

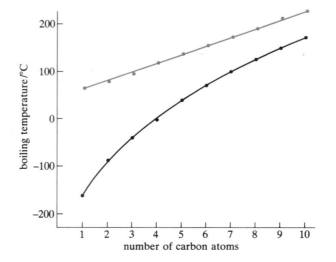

FIGURE 12 Plots of boiling temperatures of linear hydrocarbons with the formula C_nH_{2n+2} (black) and linear alcohols with the formula $C_nH_{2n+1}OH$ (red) against the number of carbon atoms, *n*.

☐ Can you explain the progressive increase in boiling temperature of the alkanes in terms of the intermolecular forces described in Section 2.2?

■ As with methane, only London forces operate between the molecules of each of the hydrocarbons. Because these forces increase with relative molecular mass, and because the difference between one alkane and the next is in each case a —CH₂— group, the smooth progression is to be expected.

☐ Can you explain the progressive increase in boiling temperature of the alcohols, and their values relative to the alkane with one more carbon atom, in terms of the intermolecular forces described in Section 2.2?

■ The difference between one alcohol and the next is still a —CH₂— group, so the progressive increase can again be attributed mainly to an increase in London forces on ascending the series. However, in each case there is hydrogen bonding involving the hydroxyl (—OH) groups in addition to the London forces. This is the reason why each alcohol has a higher boiling temperature than the corresponding alkane with one more carbon atom (the relative molecular masses are almost the same).

One characteristic of a homologous series, then, is a progressive increase in boiling temperature. What about solubilities? In Units 13–14, you carried out some experiments to investigate the solubility of various substances in water and in heptane. If you were to do this for the six alcohols in Table 6, all of which are liquids, you would find that methanol, ethanol and propan-1-l are completely soluble in water, that is, soluble in all proportions. However, moving further up the series from butan-1-ol to hexan-1-ol, you would find that solubility decreases, such that hexan-1-ol is only slightly soluble. Consequently, as progressively more of the alcohol is added to the water, a point is reached where no more will dissolve, resulting in two liquid layers. By contrast, only methanol is not completely soluble in heptane. What then governs the solubility of one liquid in another? Again, as with boiling temperatures, it is the intermolecular forces that are important.

You will recall from Units 13–14 that many ionic substances, such as sodium chloride, dissolve in water. But the attractive forces between positive and negative ions are very strong (hence the high melting and boiling temperatures of these substances), so what causes them to separate and go into solution? You might have spotted a clue from the fact that ionic substances are not soluble in non-polar solvents. An ionic substance dissolves in a polar solvent, such as water, because the strong electrical attraction between the ions and the strong dipole–dipole forces between the solvent molecules are replaced by correspondingly strong forces between the ions and the (polar) solvent (Figure 13).

☐ Why do you suppose ionic compounds are not soluble in non-polar substances?

■ The strong forces between the ions cannot be compensated by the weak forces between ions and (non-polar) solvent. These observations are summarized in the rule of thumb 'like dissolves like'.

ITQ 2 Dry-cleaning involves the use of an organic solvent (usually 1,1,1-trichloroethane, CCl_3CH_3, the solvent that you used in the tin iodide experiment in Units 13–14) rather than an aqueous cleanser. What does this imply about the nature of the soiling matter that dry-cleaning removes?

Similar considerations govern the solubilities of the linear alcohols in water. The predominant intermolecular forces between water molecules are the hydrogen bonds between the hydrogen atom of the —OH group of one molecule and the oxygen atom of another. The molecules of methanol, ethanol and propan-1-ol are small enough that relatively few water–water hydrogen bonds need to be broken and this disruption is adequately compensated by the water–alcohol hydrogen bonds that can be formed.

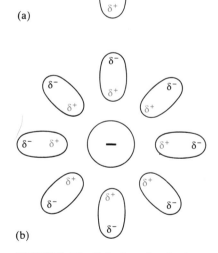

(a)

(b)

FIGURE 13 Solution of an ionic compound in a polar solvent. The ions are surrounded by a cluster of solvent molecules. The negative ends of solvent molecule dipoles point towards the cations (a), and the positive ends of solvent molecule dipoles point towards the anions (b).

However, on moving up the series, the progressive increase in length of the hydrocarbon groups means that more and more hydrogen bonds between water molecules need to be broken, and, by the time hexan-1-ol is reached, the alcohol–water hydrogen bonds are too few to compensate. Consequently, butan-1-ol, pentan-1-ol and hexan-1-ol are incompletely soluble in water, resulting in two liquid layers.

☐ Why do you suppose that, of the six alcohols in Table 6, only methanol is not completely soluble in heptane?

■ The hydrogen-bonding between the alcohol molecules, with the exception of methanol, must be a relatively small proportion of the total intermolecular forces. Consequently, the less specific London forces between the alcohol molecules and heptane molecules are able to compensate for their disruption. Only for methanol, CH_3—OH, is hydrogen-bonding the predominant force, leading to incomplete solubility in heptane.

These two physical properties, boiling temperature and solubility, were chosen as examples of a general phenomenon: *the physical properties of the members of a homologous series change in a regular manner up the series.* But we shall find that the concept of a homologous series is most useful when we come to look at *chemical* properties in Section 6.

First, though, we are going to spend some time looking in more detail at the tremendous variety found in the molecular structures of carbon compounds, how these can be organized according to a small number of straightforward rules, and why this variety of form is important.

SAQ 9 Can you explain why hexadecan-1-ol, CH_3—$(CH_2)_{14}$—CH_2—OH, is only partially soluble in methanol, CH_3—OH, but is completely soluble in heptane?

"WE SHOULD BE THANKFUL . WHAT IF OIL AND WATER DID MIX ! "

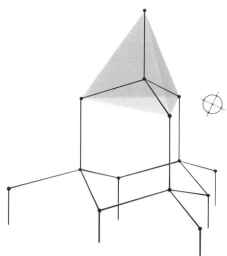

FIGURE 14 The structure of diamond. Each carbon atom is surrounded by four others located at the corners of a tetrahedron, as indicated by the portion at the top shaded pink.

3.3 STRUCTURAL ISOMERISM

For this Section, you will need the molecular model kit, the stereoviewer and filmstrip 1, all from Tray C of the Experiment Kit, together with Tape 3 and a cassette player.

So far, because we have been considering *linear* molecules, we have been content to represent them by their structural formulae, without being concerned about the detailed arrangement of the atoms in space, or, in other words, molecular shape. But we are now going to look at molecules in which the carbon backbone has branches. In order to be able to do this, you must first learn something of the shape of such molecules, and, in particular, the way in which the bonds to an individual carbon atom are arranged.

☐ In Units 13–14, you were told the arrangement of the bonds to the carbon atoms in diamond. Can you recall what this is?

■ In diamond, each atom has four bonds which point towards the corners of a tetrahedron (Figure 14).

As in diamond, each carbon atom in an organic compound with four single bonds to other atoms has these bonds pointing to the four corners of a tetrahedron. Consequently, *the structural formulae that we have been using up to now are two-dimensional representations of three-dimensional objects.*

Now, just as a (2-D) photograph of a (3-D) object from the front will in general look different from one taken from the side, so it is with molecules (Figure 15). So, one of the skills that anyone beginning to study organic compounds must acquire is the ability, when looking at different structural formulae, to recognize those which are apparently different but actually represent the same molecule. The best way to acquire this skill is to use a molecular model kit; that is why one has been included in your Experiment Kit. A little practice with molecular models should soon enable you to interpret structural formulae with confidence. You will then be in a position to recognize when two structural formulae do in fact represent two different molecules. This is necessary in order to understand the phenomenon known as structural isomerism.

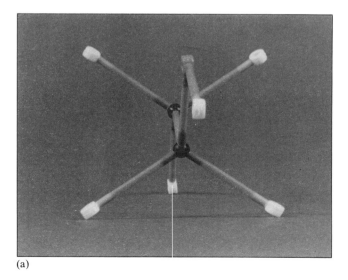

(a)

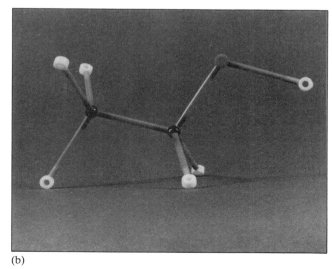

(b)

FIGURE 15 Photographs of a molecular model of ethanol: (a) front view; (b) side view.

Terms in AV sequence:

CONFORMATION

STRUCTURAL ISOMERS

SKELETAL ISOMERS

POSITION ISOMERS

FUNCTIONAL ISOMERS

ETHER

You should now work through the first AV sequence for these two Units, entitled 'Structural formulae and molecular structures', which you will find on Tape 3 (Side 1, Band 2). It begins by introducing the molecular model kit, and gives you practice in making a model of a molecule, given its structural formula. It then goes on to deal with the phenomenon of structural isomerism. This sequence is quite long and will probably take about 1 hour in all, so you might like to take a break after Frame 6. Note that whenever you are asked to make up a model, you should stop the tape and then restart it when your model is complete.

Contents of molecular model kit

	Atomic centres *	
Shape	Colour	Element
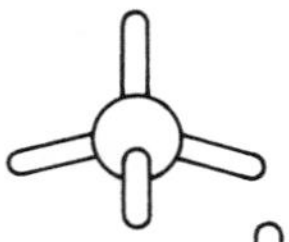	black	carbon (C)
	blue	nitrogen (N)
	red	oxygen (O)
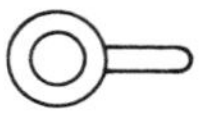	white	hydrogen (H)
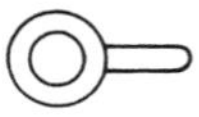	light green	fluorine (F)
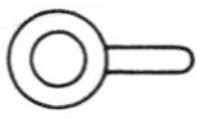	green	chlorine (Cl)
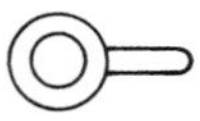	blue-green	bromine (Br)
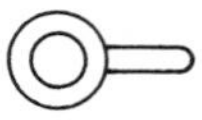	dark green	iodine (I)

* Your particular model kit may contain atomic centres with cylindrically-shaped hubs or spherically-shaped hubs, or there may be some of each. The two types are interchangeable; the important features are the colour of the atomic centres and the number of prongs they have, not the shape of the hub to which the prongs are attached.

You may also be unsure about the distinction made between blue-green and dark green; the blue-green centres are just a little darker than the green ones; the dark green ones are very much darker.

2   Alkane structures

(a)   methane   (b)   ethane

In ethane, rotation about the C—C bond of one half relative to the other gives a number of different geometries — these are called *conformations*.

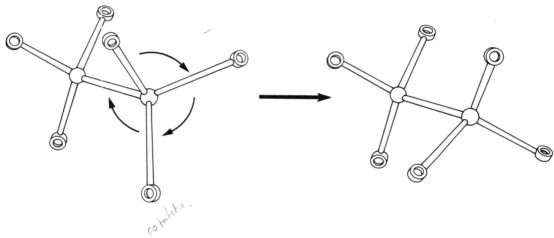

two different conformations of the ethane molecule — interconversion simply involves rotation of one half of the molecule relative to the other

(c)   (d)

propane

structural formulae with carbon atoms in the same sequence (order) are the same

3   Fluoromethane, CH₃F   *Same*

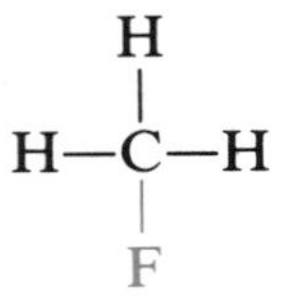

H–C–H with H top, F bottom (a)

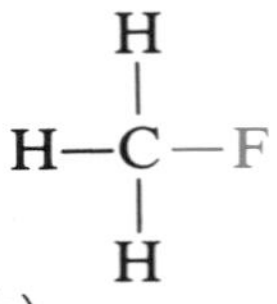

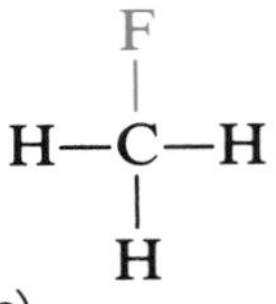

H–C–F with H top, H bottom (b)

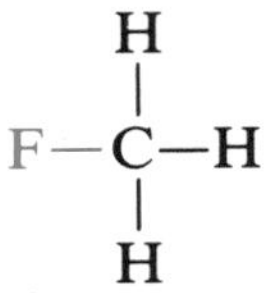

H–C–H with F top, H bottom (c)

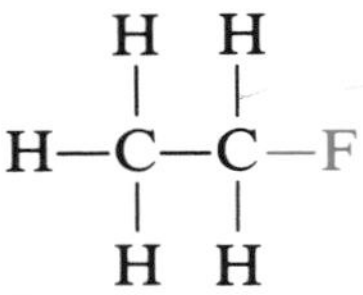

F–C–H with H top, H bottom (d)

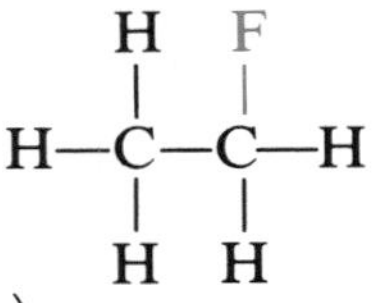

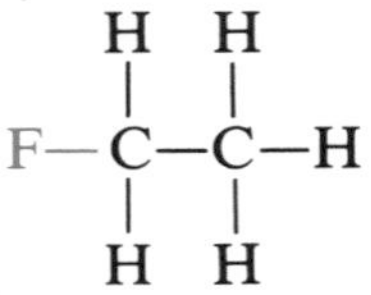

4   Fluoroethane, C₂H₅F   *equivalent*

a c same

b

(a) H–C–C–F

(b) H–C–C–H

(c) F–C–C–H

5   Structures with molecular formula C₃H₇F

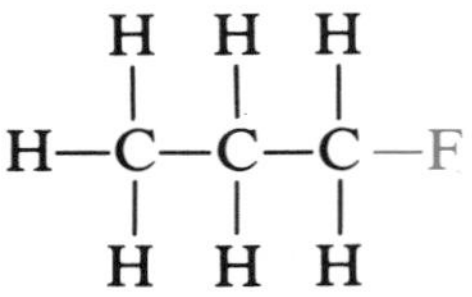

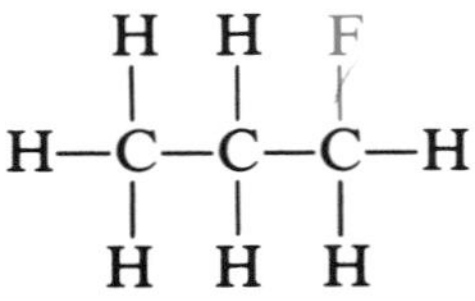

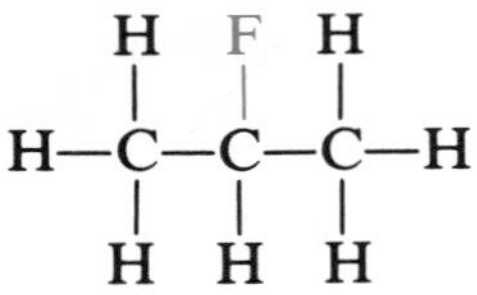

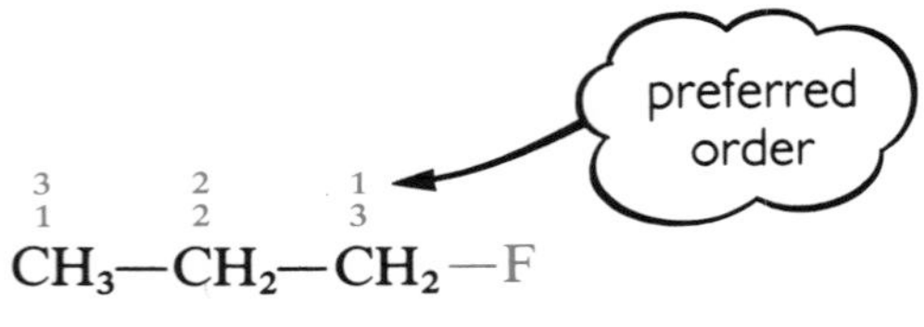

Flori attached
end carbon

(a) H–C–C–C–F

(b) H–C–C–C–H

F attached second ?

(c) H–C–C–C–H

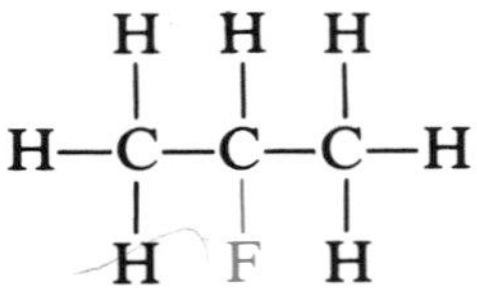

(d) H–C–C–C–H

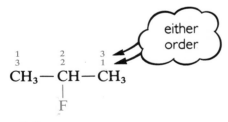

$$\overset{3}{\underset{1}{C}}H_3 - \overset{2}{\underset{2}{C}}H_2 - \overset{1}{\underset{3}{C}}H_2 - F$$

I-fluoropropane

$$\overset{1}{\underset{3}{C}}H_3 - \overset{2}{\underset{2}{C}}H - \overset{3}{\underset{1}{C}}H_3$$
|
F

2-fluoropropane

The order of numbering is chosen to give the lowest number to the point of attachment of the functional group.

6 Structural isomers

Same molecular formula, C_3H_7F

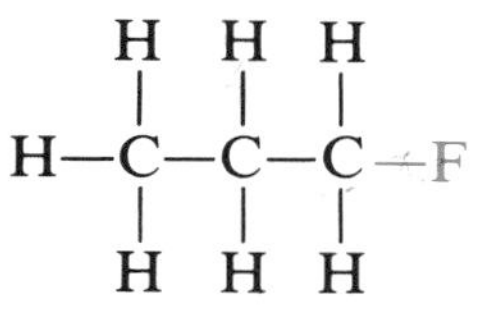

$$H-\underset{\underset{H}{|}}{\overset{\overset{H}{|}}{C}}-\underset{\underset{H}{|}}{\overset{\overset{H}{|}}{C}}-\underset{\underset{H}{|}}{\overset{\overset{H}{|}}{C}}-F$$

1-fluoropropane

$$H-\underset{\underset{H}{|}}{\overset{\overset{H}{|}}{C}}-\underset{\underset{H}{|}}{\overset{\overset{F}{|}}{C}}-\underset{\underset{H}{|}}{\overset{\overset{H}{|}}{C}}-H$$

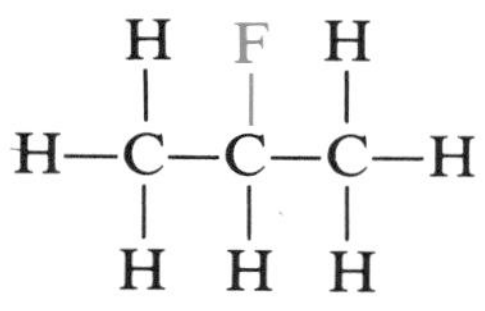

2-fluoropropane

The atoms are connected in a different order

They are called STRUCTURAL ISOMERS

Interconversion of models of these molecules
involves breaking and reforming bonds

7 | Structures with molecular formula C_4H_9F

☐ Which of these structures represent identical molecules?

■ ....

☐ Which are structural isomers?

■ ....

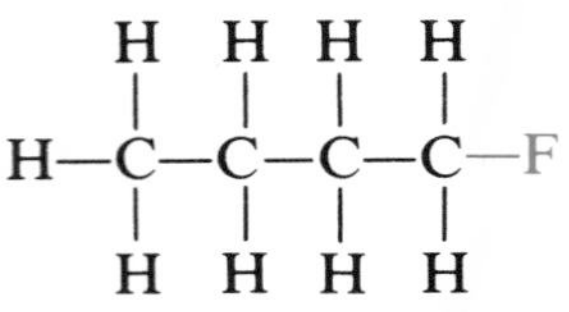

$$
\begin{array}{cccc}
& H & H & H & H \\
& | & | & | & | \\
H- & C- & C- & C- & C-F \\
& | & | & | & | \\
& H & H & H & H
\end{array}
$$

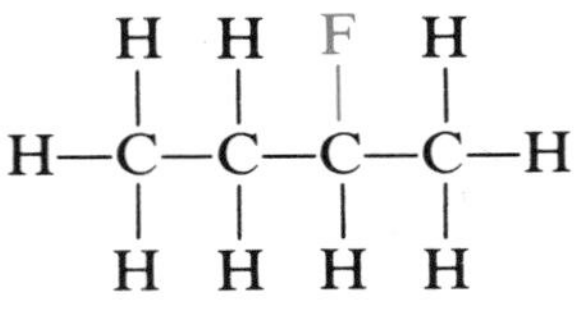

(a)

$$
\begin{array}{cccc}
& H & H & F & H \\
& | & | & | & | \\
H- & C- & C- & C- & C-H \\
& | & | & | & | \\
& H & H & H & H
\end{array}
$$

(b)

$$
\begin{array}{ccc}
F & H & H \\
| & | & | \\
H-C- & C- & C-H \\
| & | & \\
H & H & H-C-H \\
& & | \\
& & H
\end{array}
$$

(c)

$$
\begin{array}{ccc}
H & H & H \\
| & | & | \\
H-C- & C- & C-F \\
| & | & | \\
H & | & H \\
& H-C-H \\
& | \\
& H
\end{array}
$$

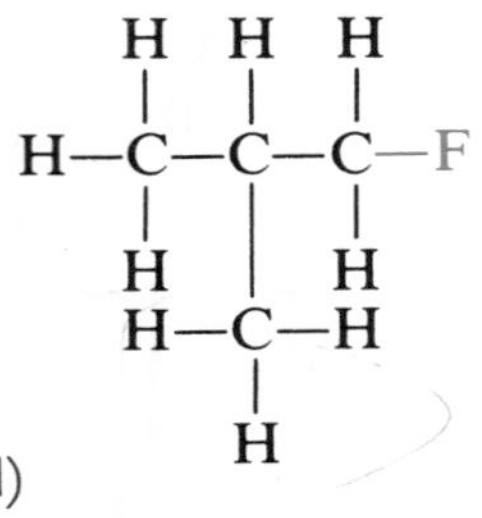

(d)

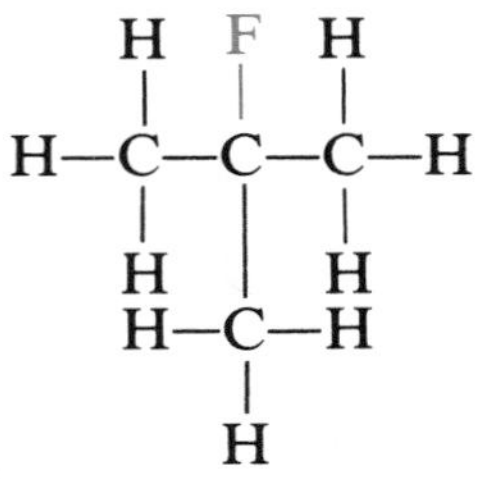

$$
\begin{array}{ccc}
H & F & H \\
| & | & | \\
H-C- & C- & C-H \\
| & | & | \\
H & | & H \\
& H-C-H \\
& | \\
& H
\end{array}
$$

(e)

$$
\begin{array}{c}
H \\
| \\
H-C-H \\
| \\
H \\
F-C-C-H \\
| \\
H \\
H-C-H \\
| \\
H
\end{array}
$$

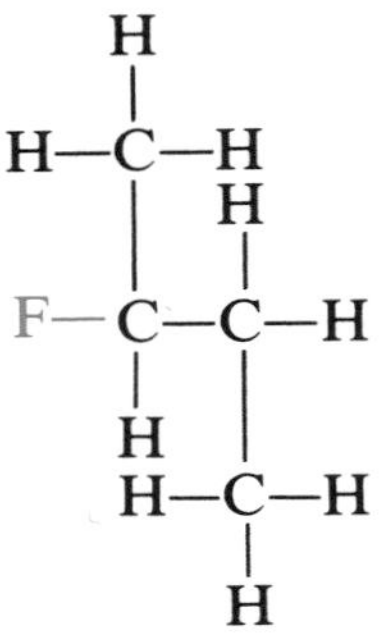

(f)

8 | Structural isomers with molecular formula C_4H_9F

(1) $CH_3-CH_2-CH_2-CH_2-F$

same as 7(a) and (c)

(2)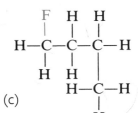

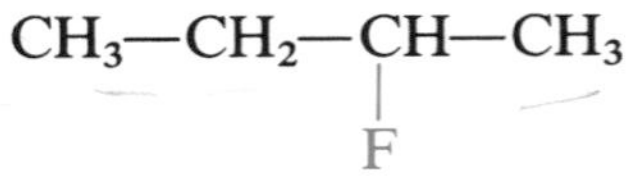

same as 7(b) and (f)

(3) 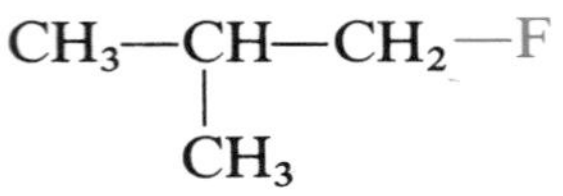 $CH_3-CH-CH_2-F$
         $|$
         CH_3

same as 7(d)

(4) 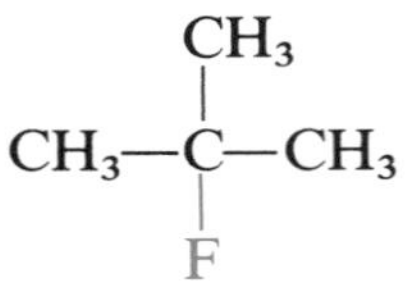 $CH_3-\overset{\displaystyle CH_3}{\underset{\displaystyle F}{C}}-CH_3$

same as 7(e)

9 Types of structural isomers

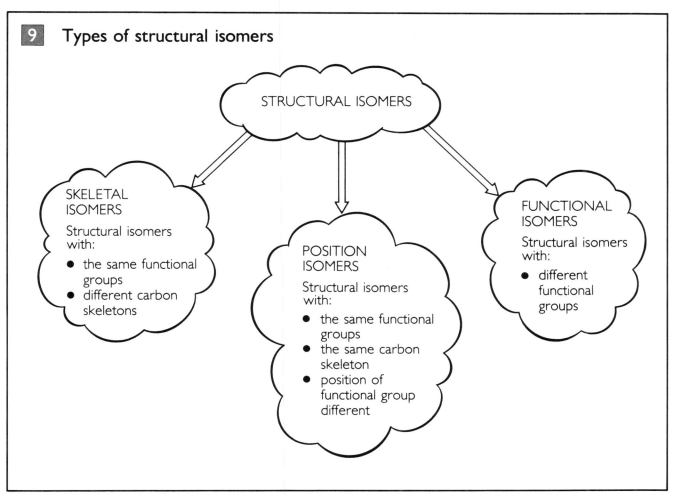

STRUCTURAL ISOMERS

SKELETAL ISOMERS

Structural isomers with:

- the same functional groups
- different carbon skeletons

POSITION ISOMERS

Structural isomers with:

- the same functional groups
- the same carbon skeleton
- position of functional group different

FUNCTIONAL ISOMERS

Structural isomers with:

- different functional groups

10 Position isomers with molecular formula C_3H_8O

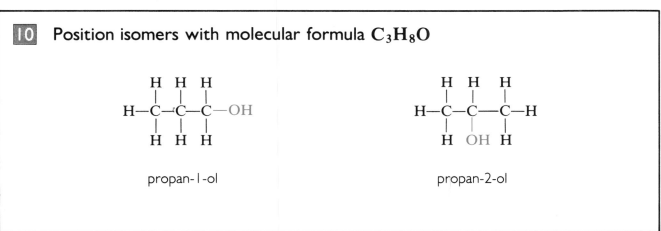

propan-1-ol

propan-2-ol

11 Functional isomers with molecular formula C_3H_8O

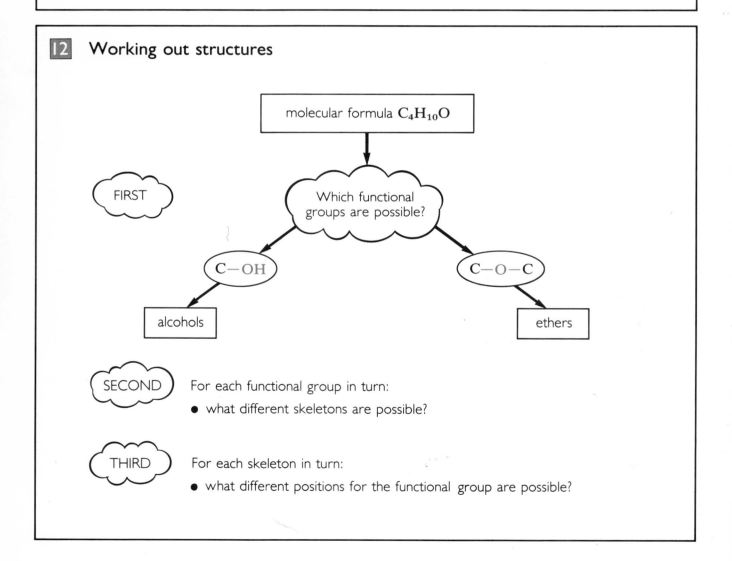

propan-1-ol

ethyl methyl ether
(methoxyethane)

Different functional
groups

12 Working out structures

molecular formula $C_4H_{10}O$

FIRST

Which functional
groups are possible?

C—OH

C—O—C

alcohols

ethers

SECOND For each functional group in turn:
● what different skeletons are possible?

THIRD For each skeleton in turn:
● what different positions for the functional group are possible?

13 Possible carbon skeletons for C₄ alcohols

☐ Which of these skeletons are different?

■ ....

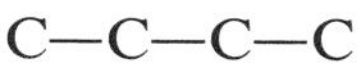

C—C—C—C

(a)

$\begin{array}{c} C \\ | \\ C—C—C \end{array}$

(b)

$\begin{array}{c} C—C \\ | \\ C—C \end{array}$

(c)

$\begin{array}{c} C \\ | \\ C—C \\ | \\ C \end{array}$

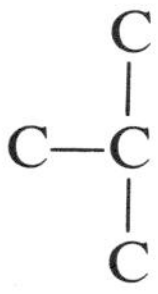

(d)

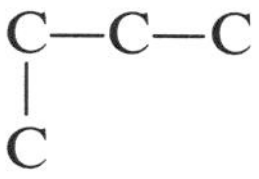

$\begin{array}{c} C—C—C \\ | \\ C \end{array}$

(e)

$\begin{array}{c} C—C—C \\ | \\ C \end{array}$

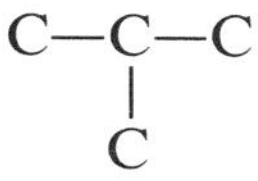

(f)

14 Possible functional group positions for C₄ alcohols

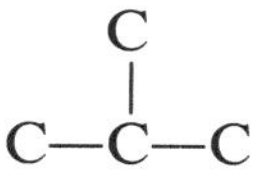

☐ Which of these structures are different?

■ ....

(1) C—C—C—C skeleton

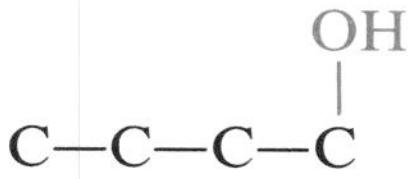

$\begin{array}{c} OH \\ | \\ C—C—C—C \end{array}$

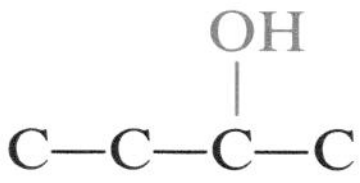

(a)

$\begin{array}{c} OH \\ | \\ C—C—C—C \end{array}$

(b)

$\begin{array}{c} OH \\ | \\ C—C—C—C \end{array}$

(c)

$\begin{array}{c} OH \\ | \\ C—C—C—C \end{array}$

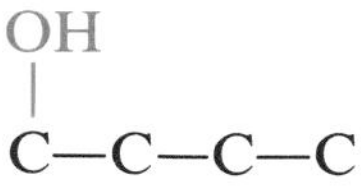

(d)

(2) 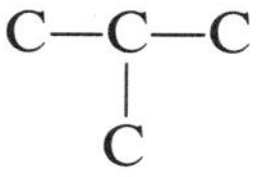 $\begin{array}{c} C—C—C \\ | \\ C \end{array}$ skeleton

$\begin{array}{c} C—C—C—OH \\ | \\ C \end{array}$

(a)

$\begin{array}{c} OH \\ | \\ C—C—C \\ | \\ C \end{array}$

(b)

$\begin{array}{c} HO—C—C—C \\ | \\ C \end{array}$

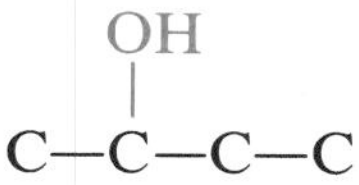

(c)

$\begin{array}{c} C—C—C \\ | \\ C—OH \end{array}$

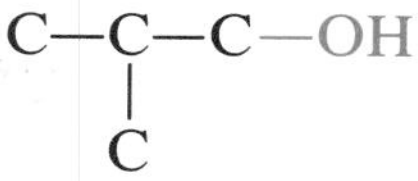

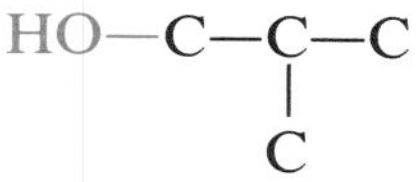

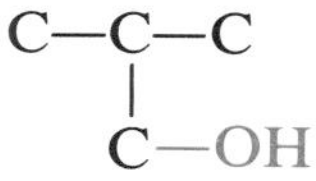

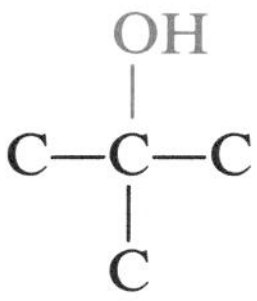

(d)

33

15 Alcohols with formula $C_4H_{10}O$

Systematic name	Older name	Formula
butan-1-ol	*n*-butyl alcohol	$CH_3-CH_2-CH_2-CH_2-OH$
butan-2-ol	sec-butyl alcohol	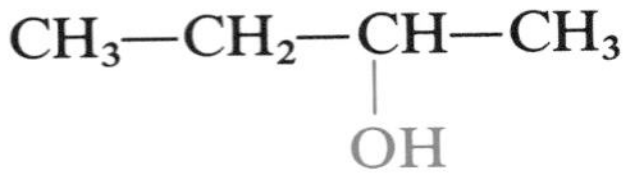 $CH_3-CH_2-CH-CH_3$ $\quad\quad\quad\quad\;\; OH$
2-methylpropan-1-ol	*iso*-butyl alcohol	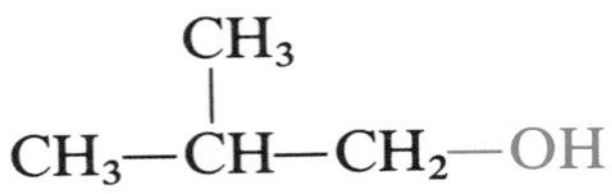 CH_3 $\;\;\;\mid$ $CH_3-CH-CH_2-OH$
2-methylpropan-2-ol	*tert*-butyl alcohol	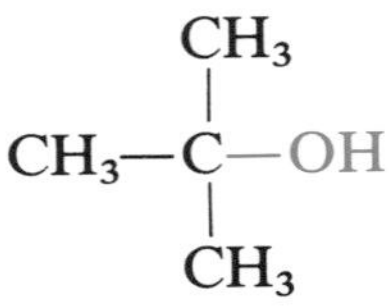 CH_3 $\;\;\;\mid$ CH_3-C-OH $\;\;\;\mid$ CH_3

16 Possible skeletons for C_4 ethers

☐ Which of these skeletons are different ?

■ ....

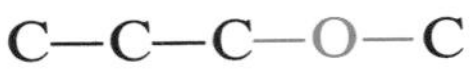

C—C—C—O—C
(a)

C—C—O—C—C
(b)

C—C—O
| |
C   C
(c)

C—C—O—C
|
C
(d)

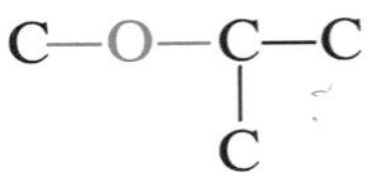

C—O—C—C
|
C
(e)

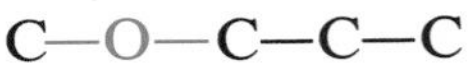

C—O—C—C—C
(f)

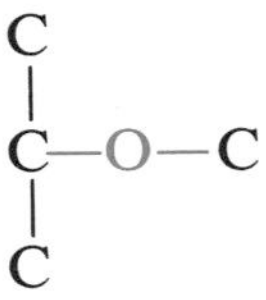

C
|
C—O—C
|
C
(g)

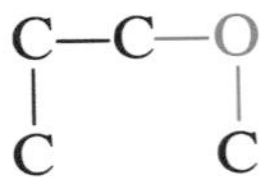

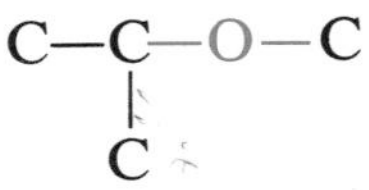

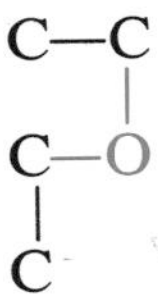

C—C
|
C—O
|
C
(h)

17 Ethers with formula $C_4H_{10}O$

Systematic name	Older name	Formula
1-methoxypropane	methyl *n*-propyl ether	$CH_3-O-CH_2-CH_2-CH_3$
ethoxyethane*	diethyl ether*	$CH_3-CH_2-O-CH_2-CH_3$
2-methoxypropane	*iso*-propyl methyl ether	$CH_3-O-CH-CH_3$ $\qquad\qquad\quad |$ $\qquad\qquad\; CH_3$

skeletal

*This is the substance commonly known as 'ether' and once widely used as an anaesthetic.

18 Summary

1 A molecular model kit is a very useful aid to visualize molecular structures.

2 Making models eventually becomes tedious and they cannot readily be used to communicate structures, so it is necessary to develop the ability to visualize molecular structures from formulae on paper.

3 First need to recognize when a given structure is the same as or different from a second with the same molecular formula.

4 For all except the smallest molecules, atoms can be put together in a variety of ways. Molecules with the same molecular formula but different structures are called structural isomers.

5 There are three kinds of structural isomers: functional isomers, skeletal isomers and position isomers.

6 When working out structures, consider first the possibility of functional isomers, then the possible skeletons, then the possible functional group positions.

DOUBLE BOND

SUMMARY OF SECTION 3

Carbon is unique among the elements in its ability to catenate, that is, to form compounds containing chains of carbon atoms bonded together. It is this property of carbon that gives rise to the enormous number and great variety of carbon compounds.

Fortunately, just as the elements are collected into families (the Groups in the Periodic Table), so there are families of carbon compounds that share common features. One particular type of family, in which members differ in a regular manner, is called a homologous series. Members of a homologous series, such as the linear alcohol series, differ by a whole number of $-CH_2-$ groups, share a common functional group, have physical properties that vary along the series in a regular manner and undergo similar chemical reactions.

Using the three types of intermolecular force described in Section 2.2, it is possible to rationalize the variation in solubilities of the members of a homologous series, in a polar solvent such as water and a non-polar solvent such as heptane. These observations are examples of the rule of thumb 'like dissolves like'.

Carbon's ability to catenate gives rise to the possibility that the same atoms may be connected together in more than one way. Compounds that share a common molecular formula, but have different structural formulae (that is, the atoms are connected together in a different sequence) are called structural isomers. Structural isomers may have a different carbon skeleton (skeletal isomers), the same skeleton but with the functional group attached to a different carbon atom (position isomers) or a different functional group (functional isomers). The phenomenon of structural isomerism further adds to the tremendous variety found among carbon compounds.

SAQ 10   For each of the six pairs of structural formulae (X1 and Y1, X2 and Y2 etc.) given below, decide which are:

A members of the same homologous series;
B position isomers;
C functional isomers;
D skeletal isomers;
E identical molecules;
F none of the above.

$CH_3-CH_2-CH_2-OH$	$CH_3-CH-CH_3$ $\quad\quad\; OH$	$CH_3-CH-CH_3$ $\quad\quad\; OH$	$CH_3-CH-OH$ $\quad\quad\; CH_3$
X1	Y1	X2	Y2

$CH_3-CH_2-CH_2-OH$	CH_3-O-CH_3	$CH_3-CH-CH_2-F$ $\quad\quad\; CH_3$	$CH_3-CH_2-CH-CH_2-F$ $\quad\quad\quad\quad\; CH_3$
X3	Y3	X4	Y4

CH_3-O-CH_3	CH_3-CH_2-OH	$CH_3-CH-CH_3$ $\quad\quad\; CH_3$	$CH_3-CH_2-CH_2-CH_3$
X5	Y5	X6	Y6

SAQ 11   Write down all the structural isomers with molecular formula C_5H_{12}.

SAQ 12   Write down the structural isomers with molecular formula C_4H_9F and identify which pairs are skeletal isomers and which pairs are position isomers.

4 DOUBLE AND TRIPLE BONDS —UNSATURATION

So far we have restricted ourselves to the study of molecules containing only single bonds. We now go on to look at the common functional groups that contain a double or a triple bond. Then we shall examine the way in which carbon–carbon double bonds can give rise to a new type of isomerism, stereoisomerism. Finally, we shall look at an example of stereoisomerism in nature.

4.1 THE STRUCTURE OF UNSATURATED COMPOUNDS

Alkenes and alkynes

So far, the idea of a covalent bond consisting of two shared electrons has been sufficient to explain the existence of a large number of carbon compounds such as the series of alcohols, for example. But when the American chemist Gilbert Lewis first proposed this concept in 1916, he knew that there were many compounds for which this idea needed extending. For example, you will recall from Section 3.1 (Table 4) that ethane has the molecular formula C_2H_6 and the abbreviated structural formula CH_3-CH_3. Now Lewis knew that there were two other hydrocarbons containing two carbon atoms, but different from ethane. These had the molecular formulae C_2H_4 and C_2H_2, respectively; that is, they had fewer hydrogen atoms per molecule than ethane. How, then, could each carbon atom achieve an octet of electrons?

You have already come across this problem, and its solution, in Units 13–14, when you considered the bonding in carbon dioxide, CO_2. The Lewis structure of CO_2 is given below.

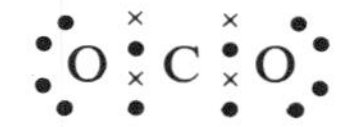

$$\ddot{\ddot{O}} \overset{\times}{\underset{\times}{\vdots}} C \overset{\times}{\underset{\times}{\vdots}} \ddot{\ddot{O}}$$

Lewis structure of CO_2

Consider first the compound C_2H_4; its systematic name is ethene, but the older name, ethylene, may be more familiar. See if you can write down its Lewis structure.

Lewis proposed that each carbon atom in ethylene shared two of its electrons with two hydrogen atoms *and the other two with the carbon atom*, as shown below.

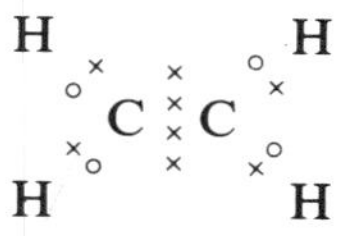

$$\begin{array}{ccc} H & & H \\ & C \overset{\times}{\underset{\times}{\vdots}} C & \\ H & & H \end{array}$$

Lewis structure of ethylene

In other words, Lewis proposed that, although the carbon–hydrogen bonds were still two-electron bonds, the carbon–carbon bond in ethylene was a four-electron bond; such a bond has twice as many electrons, so it is called a **double bond**. The full and abbreviated structural formulae of ethylene are given below.

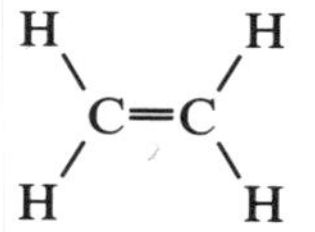

$$\begin{array}{ccc} H & & H \\ \diagdown & & \diagup \\ & C = C & \\ \diagup & & \diagdown \\ H & & H \end{array} \qquad\qquad CH_2 = CH_2$$

structural formula of ethylene   abbreviated structural formula of ethylene

The systematic name for the compound C_2H_2 is ethyne, though the older name, acetylene, is probably more familiar. Can you suggest what the Lewis structure of acetylene might be?

37

TRIPLE BOND

SATURATED COMPOUND

UNSATURATED COMPOUND

ALKENE

ALKYNE

CARBONYL GROUP

ALDEHYDE

KETONE

CARBOXYLIC ACID

CARBOXYL GROUP

ALKANAL

ALKANONE

As there are only two atoms of hydrogen in acetylene, each carbon atom needs to share three electrons with the other, forming a six-electron bond, or a **triple bond**. You have already come across a triple bond in the nitrogen molecule, N_2, in Units 13–14. The Lewis structure, structural formula and abbreviated structural formula of acetylene are shown below.

$$H \overset{\times}{\underset{\circ}{\times}} C \overset{\times}{\underset{\times}{\times}} C \overset{\circ}{\underset{\times}{\times}} H \qquad H-C \equiv C-H \qquad CH \equiv CH$$

Lewis structure of acetylene   structural formula of acetylene   abbreviated structural formula of acetylene

In ethane each carbon atom is attached to four other atoms: it is said to be a **saturated compound**. In ethylene and acetylene on the other hand, the carbon atoms are attached to three and two atoms, respectively: they are said to be **unsaturated compounds**.* The double and triple bonds are considered to be functional groups, since they are reactive centres: the unreactive hydrocarbon group discussed in Section 2.1 must be a saturated group. For example, ethylene and acetylene both react with bromine whereas ethane does not:

$$CH_2{=}CH_2 + Br_2 \longrightarrow Br{-}CH_2{-}CH_2{-}Br$$
ethylene

$$CH \equiv CH + 2Br_2 \longrightarrow \underset{\underset{Br}{|}}{Br{-}CH}{-}\underset{\underset{Br}{|}}{CH}{-}Br$$
acetylene

$$CH_3{-}CH_3 + Br_2 \longrightarrow \text{no reaction}$$
ethane

As with the other functional groups you have met, ethylene and acetylene both give rise to homologous series. The class of compounds which contains the group $\overset{\diagdown}{\underset{\diagup}{C}}{=}\overset{\diagup}{\underset{\diagdown}{C}}$ is known as the **alkenes**, and the class of compounds which contains the group $-C{\equiv}C-$ is known as the **alkynes**. The first few linear alkenes and linear alkynes are shown in Table 8. The alkenes, particularly ethylene and propylene, are manufactured on an enormous scale as chemical building blocks for use in a whole variety of products. Ethylene is the single most important organic compound produced industrially: worldwide production in 1985 was 44 million tonnes.

TABLE 8   Some alkenes and alkynes

Alkenes			Alkynes		
Systematic name	Older name	Formula	Systematic name	Older name	Formula
ethene	ethylene	$CH_2{=}CH_2$	ethyne	acetylene	$CH{\equiv}CH$
propene	propylene	$CH_3{-}CH{=}CH_2$	propyne	—	$CH_3{-}C{\equiv}CH$
but-1-ene*	—	$CH_3{-}CH_2{-}CH{=}CH_2$	but-1-yne*	—	$CH_3{-}CH_2{-}C{\equiv}CH$

* The numeral identifies the position of the first carbon atom of the double or triple bond.

Each alkene or alkyne derives its systematic name from the corresponding alkane by changing the final -*ane* to -*ene* (for alkenes) or -*yne* (for alkynes). So the alkene corresponding to eth*ane* is eth*ene*, and the alkyne is eth*yne*. However, for chains longer than three carbons, it is necessary to include a positional number to indicate the *first* of the two carbon atoms involved in the double or triple bond.

So, $\overset{4}{C}H_3{-}\overset{3}{C}H_2{-}\overset{2}{C}H{=}\overset{1}{C}H_2$ is called but-1-ene (pronounced 'beaut-one-een') whereas $\overset{4}{C}H_3{-}\overset{3}{C}H{=}\overset{2}{C}H{-}\overset{1}{C}H_3$ is called but-2-ene. The number is chosen to be as low as possible so but-4-ene for the former, or but-3-ene for the latter, would be incorrect names. Analogously, the compound with formula $CH_3-CH_2-C\equiv CH$ is called but-1-yne (pronounced 'beaut-one-ine') whereas $CH_3-C\equiv C-CH_3$ is called but-2-yne. Following general practice, we shall use systematic names for the alkenes and alkynes, except for ethylene, propylene and acetylene where the older name is in general use.

Aldehydes, ketones and carboxylic acids

As you have already seen, double and triple bonds can involve atoms other than carbon. By far the most important example in organic chemistry is the carbon–oxygen double bond, called the **carbonyl group**. The simplest carbon compound containing a carbonyl group is formaldehyde.

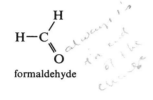
formaldehyde

Formaldehyde is the first member of the **aldehyde** series. Its structural formula is shown in the margin. The characteristic functional group of aldehydes is the carbonyl group ($C=O$) with a hydrogen atom

attached, $-C\begin{smallmatrix}H\\ \\O\end{smallmatrix}$ (further abbreviated to $-CH=O$ in these Units). This

leaves one spare valency to attach a hydrocarbon group. But there is a group of compounds in which the carbonyl group is attached to two hydro-

carbon groups ($C-C\begin{smallmatrix}C\\ \\O\end{smallmatrix}$); these are called **ketones**. The simplest ketone is

acetone, which has the structural formula shown in the margin.

$CH_3-C\begin{smallmatrix}CH_3\\ \\O\end{smallmatrix}$

acetone

The third important class of compounds containing the carbonyl group is the **carboxylic acids**. The functional group of the carboxylic acids is a composite one consisting of an $-OH$ group attached to a $C=O$ group.

$-C\begin{smallmatrix}O\\ \\OH\end{smallmatrix}$

carboxyl group

The properties of this composite group are sufficiently different from those of the separate component groups ($-OH$ and $C=O$) that it is given a distinct name, the **carboxyl group**. The first member of this series is formic acid, which is the active ingredient in ant venom and nettle stings. The second is acetic acid; vinegar is essentially a dilute solution of acetic acid in water. (You have already come across acetic acid in Unit 15 where it was represented simply as HAc.)

$H-C\begin{smallmatrix}OH\\ \\O\end{smallmatrix}$
formic acid

$CH_3-C\begin{smallmatrix}OH\\ \\O\end{smallmatrix}$
acetic acid

As with previous classes of compounds, the aldehydes, ketones and carboxylic acids are all named by appropriately modifying the name of the parent hydrocarbon. Aldehydes are named by replacing the final -e in the alkane name by -al: so the first member of the series is methan*al*, derived from methan*e*, and the systematic name for the series is **alkanals**, from alkan*es*.

☐ What is the name of the aldehyde with six carbon atoms?

■ The corresponding alkane is hexane, so the aldehyde is hexanal.

$$CH_3-CH_2-CH_2-CH_2-CH_2-CH=O$$

hexanal

Because the name takes account of the carbon atom of the carbonyl group, this naming procedure can only be used if the carbonyl group is at the end of the chain. If it is attached elsewhere, the naming procedure becomes more complicated. But for ketones, since the carbonyl group can be anywhere in the chain, a positional number is necessary for a chain of more than four carbon atoms. The name is derived from the alkane with the same number of carbon atoms by replacing the final -e by -one (pronounced 'own'). So the systematic name for the simplest ketone, which has three carbon atoms, is propan*one* (from propan*e*); similarly the systematic name for the series is **alkanones**, from alkan*es*.

☐ There are two possible ketones with five carbon atoms. See if you can work out what they are, and then name them. (You will need to include a positional number; this is done in an analogous way to the naming of alcohols.)

■ Both ketones are called pentanone (from pentane): one is pentan-2-one and the other is pentan-3-one. (Pentan-4-one is the same as pentan-2-one, so we choose the name with the smaller number).

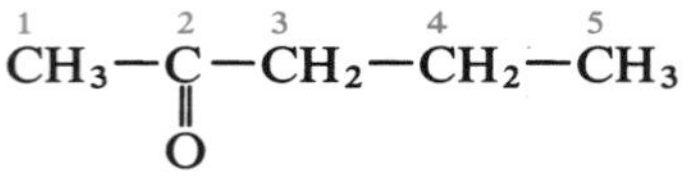

$$\overset{1}{C}H_3 - \overset{2}{C} - \overset{3}{C}H_2 - \overset{4}{C}H_2 - \overset{5}{C}H_3$$
$$\|$$
$$O$$

pentan-2-one

$$\overset{1}{C}H_3 - \overset{2}{C}H_2 - \overset{3}{C} - \overset{4}{C}H_2 - \overset{5}{C}H_3$$
$$\|$$
$$O$$

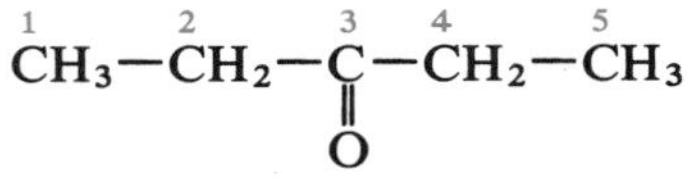

pentan-3-one

Carboxylic acids are named in a similar way to aldehydes; again, the simple procedure can only be used if the carboxyl group is at the end of the chain. The name is obtained by replacing the final -e in the name of the alkane with the same number of carbons with -oic acid (pronounced 'oh-ic acid'). So the simplest acid is methanoic acid, from methane.

☐ What is the name of the carboxylic acid with ten carbon atoms?

■ The corresponding alkane is decane, so the acid is decanoic acid.

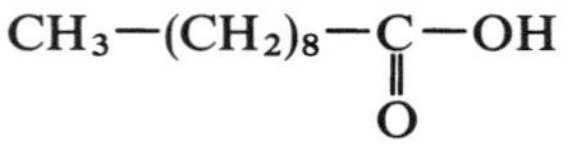

$$CH_3 - (CH_2)_8 - C - OH$$
$$\|$$
$$O$$

decanoic acid

As before, we shall follow general practice and use systematic names for the individual aldehydes, ketones and carboxylic acids, except for formaldehyde, acetaldehyde, acetone, formic acid and acetic acid, where the older name is in general use; we shall similarly use the older names for the three series.

Unsaturated compounds play an enormously important role both in nature and in manufactured materials. Carboxylic acids, for example, are essential building blocks for proteins and synthetic fibres, both of which will be discussed in more detail in Section 7.

Many of the more important unsaturated compounds contain more than one site of unsaturation. One group that occurs frequently in such compounds is the **phenyl group**, a structure in which three carbon–carbon double bonds alternate with three single bonds in a six-membered ring (Figure 16). Some compounds containing the phenyl group are shown in Figure 17, using three different representations. Note that the abbreviated structural formulae use a special symbol for the phenyl group, a hexagon with three extra lines parallel to each alternate side; each vertex corresponds to a carbon atom, and each bond not explicitly shown is assumed to be attached to a hydrogen atom. Frequently, the abbreviation Ph— is used to denote the phenyl group (Figure 17).

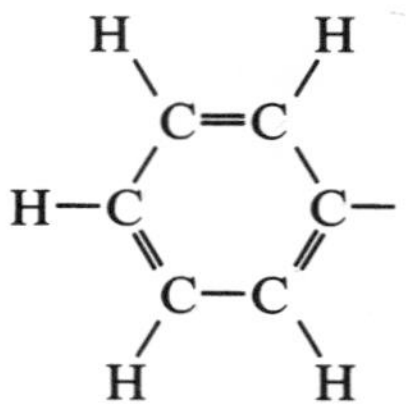

FIGURE 16   The phenyl group.

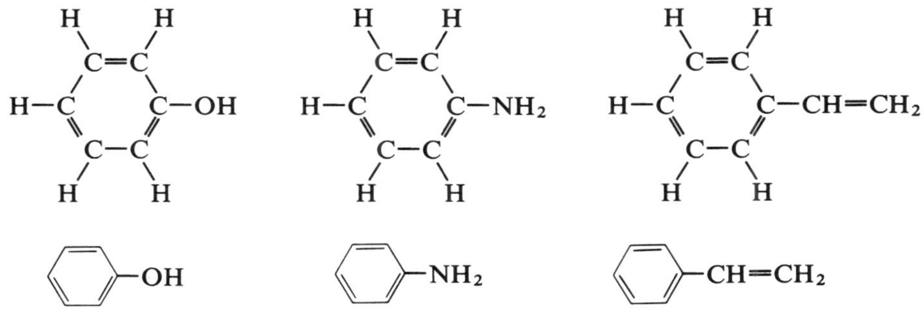

FIGURE 17 Some compounds containing the phenyl group, each represented in three different ways.

SAQ 13 Classify each of the structures 1–6 below as one of the following types of compound:

A alkane   E alkylamine
B alkene   F aldehyde
C alkyne   G ketone
D alcohol   H carboxylic acid

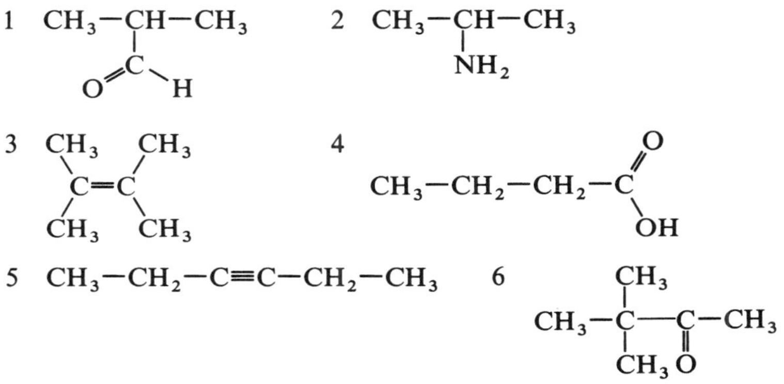

SAQ 14 Pentan-2-one and pentan-3-one have the same molecular formulae but different structural formulae, so they must be structural isomers. Which of the three types of structural isomers are they?

4.2 ISOMERISM IN UNSATURATED COMPOUNDS

For this Section, you will need the molecular model kit, the stereoviewer and filmstrip 1 from the Experimental Kit, together with Tape 3 and a cassette player.

Just as you saw earlier with compounds containing functional groups, structural isomerism can also occur in compounds containing carbon–carbon multiple bonds. For example, the three compounds below all have the molecular formula C_4H_8.

$$CH_3-CH_2-CH=CH_2 \qquad CH_3-CH=CH-CH_3 \qquad CH_2=C\begin{smallmatrix}CH_3\\\\CH_3\end{smallmatrix}$$

but-1-ene   but-2-ene   2-methylpropene

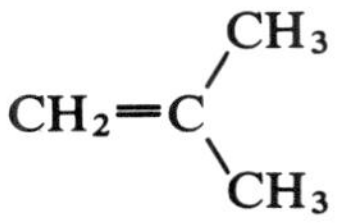

Terms in AV sequence:

STEREOISOMERS

GEOMETRIC ISOMERS

CIS ISOMER

TRANS ISOMER

You may remember that but-1-ene, $CH_3-CH_2-CH=CH_2$, was listed in Table 8.

☐ Decide whether each of but-2-ene and 2-methylpropene is a functional, skeletal or position isomer of but-1-ene.

■ They both have the same functional group (C=C) as but-1-ene, so they are not functional isomers. But-2-ene has the same backbone, so it is a position isomer of but-1-ene; 2-methylpropene has a different backbone, so it is a skeletal isomer of but-1-ene.

You have already come across the possibility of structural isomerism within ketones in SAQ 14. What you may not have noticed is that aldehydes and ketones with the same number of carbon atoms are also structural isomers.

What type of structural isomerism do you think relates propanal and acetone (propanone)?

$$CH_3-CH_2-\underset{\underset{\displaystyle O}{\|}}{C}H \qquad CH_3-\underset{\underset{\displaystyle O}{\|}}{C}-CH_3$$

propanal   acetone (propanone)

Because they both have the same carbon backbone, they are clearly not skeletal isomers. The key question is: Do they have the same functional group or different ones? Since they have carbonyl groups you may have decided that they have the same functional group. In fact, it turns out that a carbonyl group at the end of a chain (in an aldehyde) is chemically different from one in the middle (in a ketone), as you will see in Section 6. So propanal and propanone are properly called functional isomers rather than position isomers.

ITQ 3   Butanal has the formula $CH_3-CH_2-CH_2-CH=O$. (a) Write down the structural formulae of the various possible aldehydes and ketones with the same molecular formula, C_4H_8O; (b) classify each of the possible structures as functional, skeletal or position isomers when compared with butanal.

ITQ 4   It is possible for another type of molecular structure to have the same molecular formula as isomeric aldehydes and ketones. For example, in addition to propanal and propanone (see above), there are the three structures (a), (b), and (c) which have the molecular formula C_3H_6O. Decide what type of isomer each of these structures is, when compared with propanal as a reference.

(a) $HO-CH_2-CH=CH_2$ (b) $CH_3-\underset{\underset{\displaystyle OH}{|}}{C}=CH_2$ (c) $CH_3-CH=CH-OH$

So, structural isomerism in unsaturated molecules is very similar to structural isomerism in saturated molecules. However, as you are about to see, unsaturated molecules containing a C=C group can sometimes give rise to another quite different type of isomerism, called *stereoisomerism*. Before we examine that, we first need to look a little more closely at the precise shape of alkenes.

You should now work through the second AV sequence for these two Units, entitled 'Geometric isomerism', which is on Tape 3 (Side 2, Band 1). It begins by looking at the detailed shape of the ethylene molecule and how it differs from the shape of the ethane molecule. It then goes on to introduce the phenomenon of stereoisomerism. As you will see in due course, there are two types of stereoisomers: this AV sequence looks at the first type, geometric isomers. This sequence should take you about 30 minutes.

19 Ethane and ethylene compared

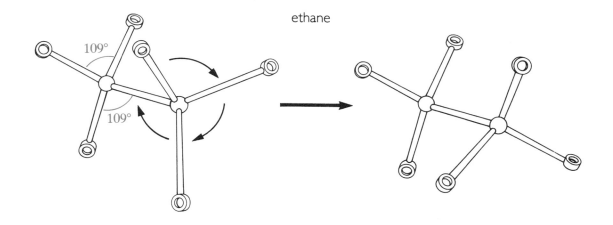

ethane

Can easily rotate one half of the molecule relative to the other

ethylene

All six atoms lie in the same plane

Cannot rotate one half of the molecule relative to the other

20 Molecular geometry

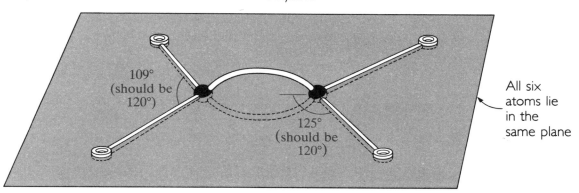

$CH_3-CH=CH_2$

propylene

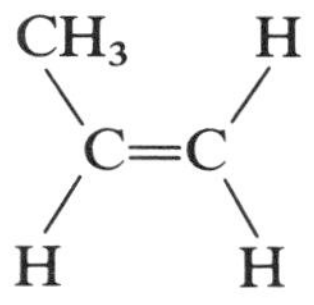

propylene

CH_3-C-CH_3
$\parallel$
O

acetone

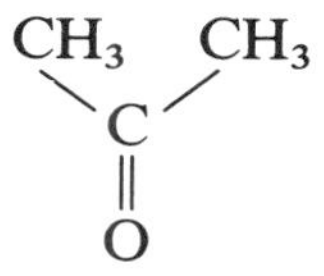

acetone

21 A new type of isomerism

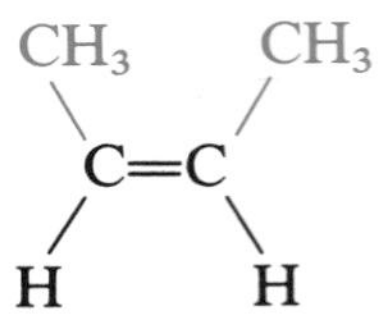

$$
\begin{array}{cc}
CH_3 & CH_3 \\
\diagdown & \diagup \\
C{=}C \\
\diagup & \diagdown \\
H & H
\end{array}
$$

(a)

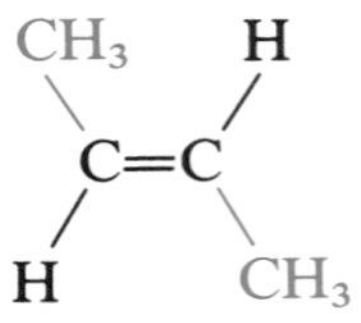

$$
\begin{array}{cc}
CH_3 & H \\
\diagdown & \diagup \\
C{=}C \\
\diagup & \diagdown \\
H & CH_3
\end{array}
$$

(b)

☐ **Are the two structures identical?**

■ No; one cannot be converted to the other without breaking bonds.

☐ **Are they isomers?**

■ Yes; they have the same molecular formula.

☐ **Are they structural isomers?**

■ No; the atoms in the carbon backbone are connected in the same sequence in both structures — that is, they have the same structural formula.

☐ **What kind of isomers are they?**

■ They are *stereoisomers*; the existence of these isomers depends on the detailed shape of the molecules. This type of stereoisomerism is called *geometric isomerism*; the two structures (a) and (b) are called *geometric isomers*.

22 Geometric isomers: *cis*- and *trans*-but-2-ene

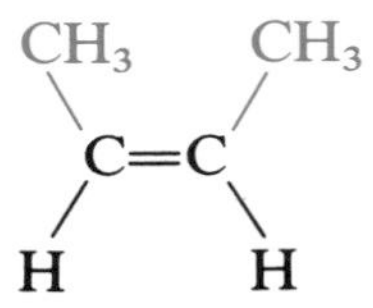

$$
\begin{array}{cc}
CH_3 & CH_3 \\
\diagdown & \diagup \\
C{=}C \\
\diagup & \diagdown \\
H & H
\end{array}
$$

cis-but-2-ene

$$
\begin{array}{cc}
CH_3 & H \\
\diagdown & \diagup \\
C{=}C \\
\diagup & \diagdown \\
H & CH_3
\end{array}
$$

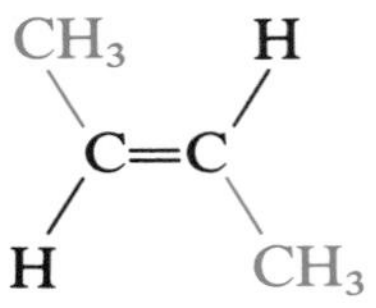

trans-but-2-ene

	cis-but-2-ene	trans-but-2-ene
boiling temperature	3.7 °C	0.9 °C
melting temperature	−138.9 °C	−105.5 °C

23 Test for geometric isomers

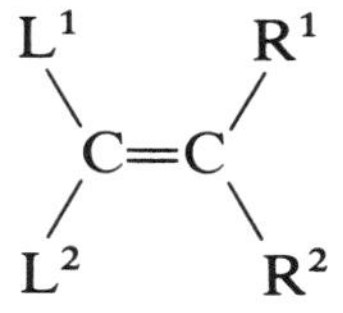

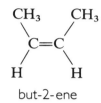

For geometric isomerism:

- the atoms or groups L^1 and L^2 must be different AND
- the atoms or groups R^1 and R^2 must be different.

24 Geometric isomers or not?

but-2-ene

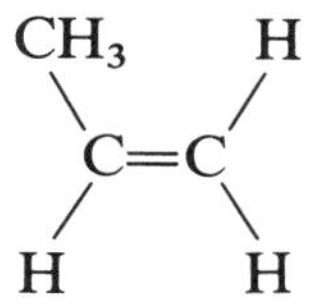

propylene

$L^1 = CH_3$ $L^2 = H$ so different

$R^1 = CH_3$ $R^2 = H$ so different

hence geometric isomers possible

$L^1 = CH_3$ $L^2 = H$ so different

$R^1 = H$ $R^2 = H$ so identical

hence geometric isomers *not* possible

25 Summary

1   A pair of *stereoisomers* have:

- the same molecular formula

- their atoms connected *in the same order*

- their atoms arranged *differently in space*

2   A pair of *geometric isomers* are stereoisomers that have:

- atoms/groups arranged differently at the ends of a double bond

SAQ 15 Examine the five pairs of formulae, X1 and Y1, X2 and Y2 etc., and decide, for each pair, which one of the statements A–E is true.

A Structures X and Y are members of a homologous series.
B Structures X and Y are structural isomers.
C Structures X and Y are geometric isomers.
D Structures X and Y are identical.
E None of the above is true.

(You may find that making models of each of the structures shown will help you answer this question.)

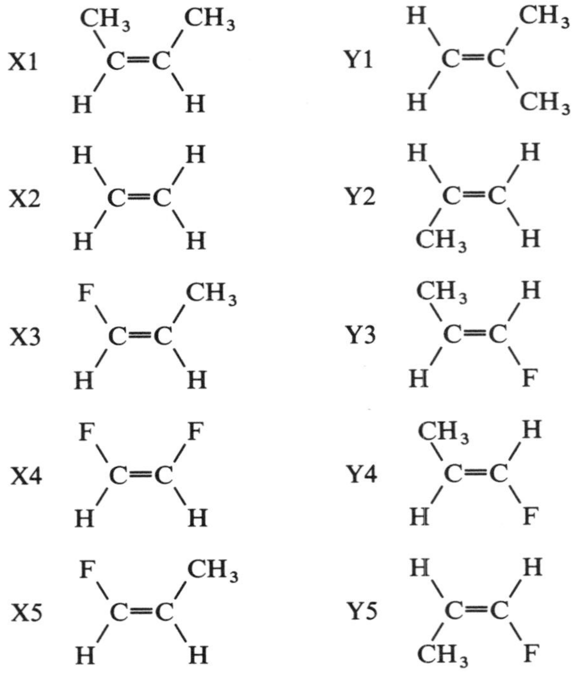

SAQ 16 There are four distinct compounds with molecular formula C_3H_5Cl, each of which has a double bond. Draw the structural formulae of the four compounds (using models as an aid if you wish) and identify which pairs are structural isomers and which pairs are geometric isomers.

SAQ 17 Esters are compounds containing the group $-\overset{\overset{\displaystyle O}{\parallel}}{C}-O-C$ in contrast to carboxylic acids which contain the group $-\overset{\overset{\displaystyle O}{\parallel}}{C}-OH$ (this is analogous to the relationship between ethers, containing the group $C-O-C$, and alcohols containing the group $C-OH$). With this in mind, draw out all the possible structures with molecular formula $C_3H_6O_2$ that are carboxylic acids or esters, and identify the isomeric relationships between the various structures.

4.3 GEOMETRIC ISOMERS IN ACTION

At this point, you may be wondering why we should bother to distinguish structures in this way—why is isomerism important? There are several reasons.

One reason is to cope with the great variety of carbon compounds. As you may recall from the Introduction to these two Units, there is a vast number of carbon compounds known. In order to make sense of them all, some method of classification or organization is needed. The most useful is the idea of a functional group and a hydrocarbon group. But this still leaves a large number of possible structures, and the concept of isomerism allows molecules to be categorized into a smaller number of groups.

Another reason relates to the need to determine the molecular structure of unknown substances. It is often the case that chemists attempt to carry out a reaction and obtain an unexpected compound as a product. Alternatively, a scientist may extract a previously unknown naturally-occurring substance, from a plant, for example.

In either situation, the problem is how to find out the molecular structure. It is not possible by any sort of microscopic examination to see individual molecules clearly enough to decipher their structure. What can be determined reasonably easily is the molecular formula. From that, and other data, chemists then consider the various possible structures with that molecular formula—in other words, the various possible isomers. By using a variety of powerful instrumental techniques, some of which you will see in the TV programme 'Organic molecules in action', it is possible to narrow down the possibilities eventually to a single structure. This approach is outlined diagrammatically in Figure 18.

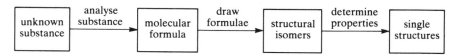

FIGURE 18   Stages in the determination of the molecular structure of an unknown compound.

Finally, the phenomenon of isomerism, particularly stereoisomerism, is of considerable importance in living systems. It is to an example that illustrates these latter two aspects that we now turn.

Among humanity's most fundamental aspirations are the assurance of an adequate food supply and the prevention of disease, aspirations threatened by a number of natural enemies. Chief among these 'pests' are certain varieties of insects. These not only carry disease, but compete for food, causing great damage to crops, both growing and in store. With the large-scale cultivation of a single crop (and, of course, subsequent storage) an infestation can spread rapidly.

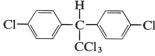
The structure of DDT

In 1939, there occurred perhaps the single most influential event in the development of insecticides, the discovery of the insecticidal activity of the substance commonly known as DDT. Its structural formula is shown in the margin. During the following three decades or so, ever-increasing amounts of DDT and other organochlorine* insecticides were used to counter insect pests such as the malaria-transmitting anopheline mosquito. It has been estimated that DDT has prevented tens of millions of deaths and protected hundreds of millions of people against malaria. Yet in most countries, the use of DDT is now banned. Why should this be so?

There are two main reasons. The first relates to the persistence of DDT and most other organochlorine insecticides in the environment. They are not readily degraded and as a consequence enter the food chains of fish, birds and other animals in ever-increasing concentrations. The second problem is one of insect resistance. There is a growing number of species of mosquito and other insects that have developed a tolerance to DDT; consequently, this insecticide is no longer effective for their control.

The development of newer pesticides with much lower persistence and toxicity such as the new synthetic pyrethroid insecticides Permethrin and Deltamethrin, discovered at the Rothamsted Experimental Station, Hertfordshire and now in world-wide use, has addressed the first of these. But the second remains a problem. One approach is to make use of compounds that the insects themselves produce, to lure them into traps or to cause them to disperse.

* Several of the early synthetic organic pesticides, such as Dieldrin, Aldrin and BHC (benzene hexachloride), share with DDT the common feature of having a molecular structure containing several chlorine atoms. For this reason, they are often referred to as organochlorine insecticides.

PHEROMONES

Many animals, including insects, communicate with their fellows by releasing certain compounds, called **pheromones**, in minute amounts. There are alarm pheromones that signal danger, sex-attractant pheromones that enable males and females to locate one another, and trail pheromones that signal the location of food.

The receptors that detect the sex-attractant pheromones are extremely sensitive. In some cases reception of just a few hundred molecules is all that is required to stimulate the male. Experiments have shown that in some species the male insect can be lured from distances as great as four kilometres. In another experiment, a single female pine saw-fly attracted more than 11 000 males! Some typical pheromone structures are shown in Tables 9 and 10.

TABLE 9   Some alarm pheromones

Insect family	Compound name	Abbreviated structural formula
Bee	nonan-2-one	$CH_3-(CH_2)_6-\overset{\displaystyle \underset{O}{\|\|}}{C}-CH_3$
Ant	hex-2-enal	$CH_3-CH_2-CH_2-CH=CH-CH=O$
Ant	4-methylheptan-3-one	$CH_3-CH_2-\overset{\displaystyle \underset{O}{\|\|}}{C}-\overset{\displaystyle \underset{CH_3}{\|}}{CH}-CH_2-CH_2-CH_3$
Ant	heptan-2-one	$CH_3-(CH_2)_4-\overset{\displaystyle \underset{O}{\|\|}}{C}-CH_3$

TABLE 10   Some insect sex attractants*

Insect	Abbreviated structural formula of compound
Honey-bee	$CH_3-\overset{\displaystyle \underset{O}{\|\|}}{C}-(CH_2)_5-CH=CH-\overset{\displaystyle \underset{O}{\|\|}}{C}-OH$
Wax-moth	$CH_3-(CH_2)_9-\overset{\displaystyle \underset{O}{\|\|}}{C}-H$
Silkworm moth	$CH_3-CH_2-CH_2-CH=CH-CH=CH-(CH_2)_8-CH_2-OH$
Peach twig borer	$CH_3-(CH_2)_3-CH=CH-(CH_2)_4-O-\overset{\displaystyle \underset{O}{\|\|}}{C}-CH_3$

* Frequently more than one compound is necessary to attract a male insect and induce it to mate. The compounds above are the sex attractants that attract the males from a great distance; other shorter-range compounds take over when the male insect is closer to the female.

Look at the formula of the second alarm pheromone in Table 9, hex-2-enal. Could this represent more than one isomer?

A more detailed structural formula of hex-2-enal shows that there are two possible isomers, shown on the next page: in one the two hydrogen atoms adjacent to the double bond are on the same side (the *cis* isomer), and in the other they are on opposite sides (the *trans* isomer). In fact, the *trans* isomer is the naturally-occurring alarm substance.

$$CH_3-CH_2-CH_2 \diagdown C=C \diagup \overset{H}{\diagup} C=O$$

cis-hex-2-enal

$$CH_3-CH_2-CH_2 \diagdown C=C \diagup \overset{H}{\diagdown} C=O$$

trans-hex-2-enal

This specificity provides the key to the use of pheromones as pest-control agents. There are a number of possibilities. One is to release the appropriate sex pheromone over the fields to be protected. This has the effect of disrupting communication and so misdirecting the male. Another is to lure the insects into traps baited with conventional pesticides. The method shown in the TV programme 'Organic molecules in action' is to use an alarm pheromone to increase the efficiency of conventional insecticides to combat aphids, the family of insects that includes the common greenfly and blackfly, which affect a large variety of crops.

Aphids are the major insect pest in arable agriculture in the United Kingdom. The damage they cause is the result both of their feeding activities and the fact that they transmit a variety of plant diseases. Existing methods of control rely on the use of so-called 'contact' insecticides such as Permethrin. Aphids are particularly difficult to eliminate from crops because they tend to cluster on the undersides of leaves. So, the plants have to be sprayed with relatively high concentrations of the insecticide, otherwise many escape simply because it does not reach them. If, however, the aphid alarm pheromone could be added to a spray mixture containing Permethrin, for example, it would cause them to become much more active (Figure 19). This would greatly increase the likelihood of the aphids coming into contact with the insecticides, and hence much lower concentrations could be used. But this would require the production of synthetic pheromone, since the insects produce it only in minute amounts. To enable this to be carried out, the active ingredient in the secretion has first to be identified.

FIGURE 19   These aphids (left) are rapidly dispersed by the application of just one drop of synthetic alarm pheromone (right).

Scientists at the Rothamsted Experimental Station, led by John Pickett, have developed a highly effective technique for identifying the active compound in the secretion produced by an aphid when it is disturbed. The method involves separating the various components using a gas chromatograph* and blowing each one in turn over a captured aphid. An electrode attached to the sensory organ of the aphid only registers a nerve

* A gas chromatograph is an instrument that enables the individual components of a complex mixture to be separated by passing them through a column (a fine tube) containing a special, non-volatile liquid. The components can be identified by the time taken to emerge from the column.

impulse in response to the true alarm pheromone. When this was done, and the active compound analysed using a mass spectrometer (Units 11–12), it was found to have a relative molecular mass of 204.36 and the molecular formula $C_{15}H_{24}$; further analysis of the data from the mass spectrometer enabled the structure to be established as a compound known as β-farnesene.

β-Farnesene has four double bonds, so for a complete specification of the structure the possibility of geometric isomers must be taken into account.

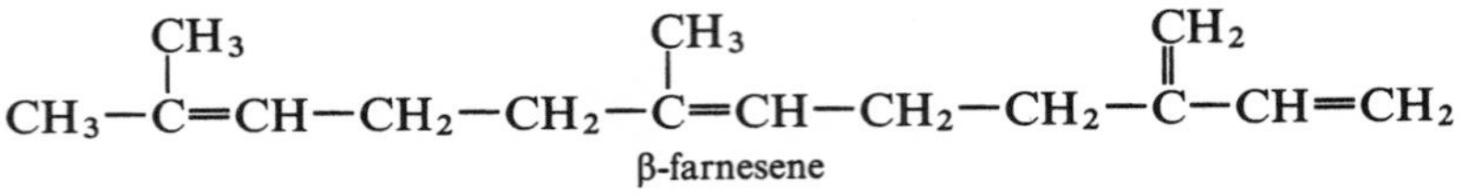

$$CH_3-\underset{\underset{CH_3}{|}}{C}=CH-CH_2-CH_2-\underset{\underset{CH_3}{|}}{C}=CH-CH_2-CH_2-\underset{\underset{CH_2}{||}}{C}-CH=CH_2$$

β-farnesene

ITQ 5 Consider first the compound penta-1,3-diene. By looking at the possible structures (a), (b) and (c) shown below, decide how many different geometric isomers there are.

(a)

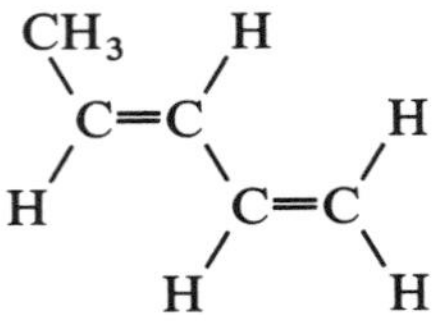

(b)

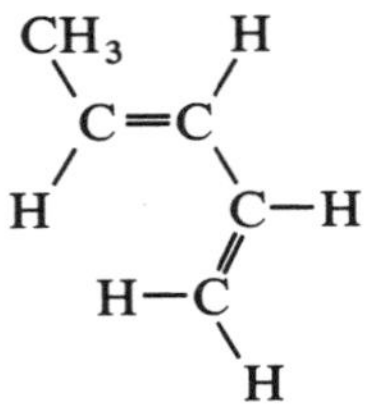

(c)

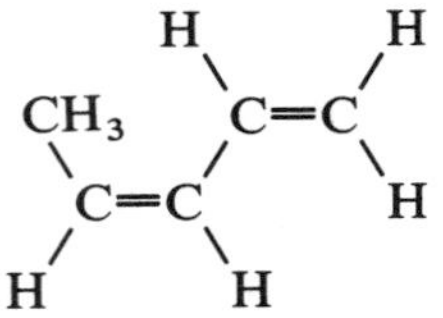

As you saw in ITQ 5, the number of possible geometric isomers for a structure with more than one double bond can be determined by considering whether each double bond in turn can give rise to *cis* or *trans* forms. Considering each of the four double bonds in β-farnesene, only one (the second from the left) has different groups at *both* ends of the double bond: the first has two methyl groups, and the third and fourth both have two hydrogen atoms at one end. As a consequence, like penta-1,3-diene, there are just two geometric isomers. These are shown below. (Remember from ITQ 5, it is the relationship of the larger of the groups at each end that determine which isomer is called *cis* and which *trans*.)

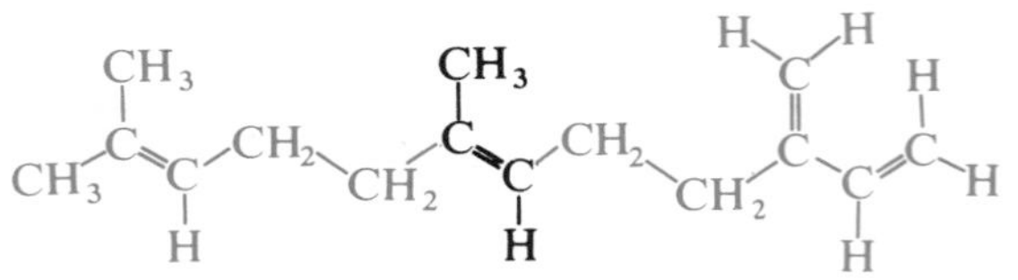

trans-β-farnesene

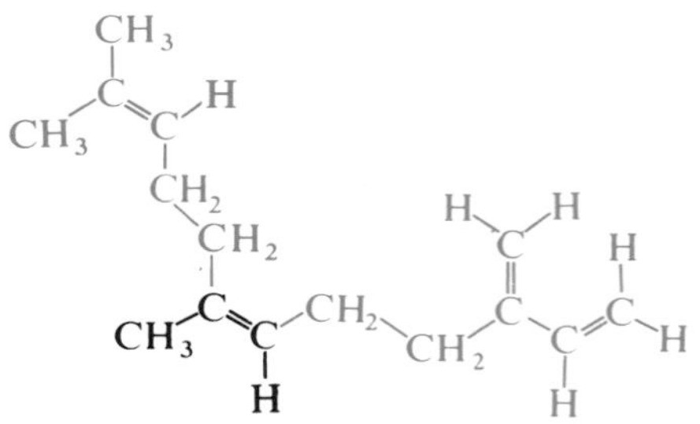

cis-β-farnesene

FIGURE 20 Comparison of an untreated plot of winter barley (left) with a plot treated with a more stable derivative of the alarm pheromone (right) (β-farnesene itself is not sufficiently stable for use directly in the field). The presence of weeds in the left-hand picture is due to damage to the crop caused by aphid-borne virus infection.

The question that remains is: Which is the alarm pheromone; is it the *cis* isomer or the *trans* isomer? When the two isomers were synthesized, only the *trans*-β-farnesene evoked a response from the aphid; the *cis* isomer was completely inactive. Molecular models of *cis*- and *trans*-β-farnesene are shown in stereoslides 10 and 11; from these, it is clear that their shapes are quite different. Since the two compounds differ only in their shape, the receptors responsible for the aphid detecting the alarm pheromone must presumably be of such a shape that only *trans*-β-farnesene fits.

Field trials have been carried out using a more stable derivative of the alarm pheromone, and with some success (Figure 20), but it remains to be seen if this particular application turns out to be commercially successful. However, few people would challenge the philosophy of using a 'copy' of a substance the aphid produces itself as a pest control agent in preference to ever-increasing amounts of pesticides.

"IF IT'S TRUE THAT THE WORLD ANT POPULATION IS 10^{15}, THEN IT'S NO WONDER WE NEVER RUN INTO ANYONE WE KNOW."

SUMMARY OF SECTION 4

The concept of a covalent bond between carbon atoms as a shared pair of electrons was extended to include four-electron (double) and six-electron (triple) carbon–carbon bonds. Such bonds constitute functional groups since they readily take part in reactions; for example, the addition of bromine to ethylene:

$$CH_2{=}CH_2 + Br_2 \longrightarrow Br{-}CH_2{-}CH_2{-}Br$$

ethylene   bromine

These functional groups give rise to the series of compounds known as the alkenes and alkynes: ethylene is the simplest of the alkenes; acetylene is the simplest of the alkynes.

Double bonds can involve atoms other than carbon, notably oxygen, giving rise to aldehydes, ketones and carboxylic acids.

Unsaturated compounds play a very important role both in nature and in manufactured materials. A commonly-occurring group in such compounds is the phenyl group, in which three carbon–carbon double bonds alternate in a six-membered ring with three single bonds.

The existence of distinct compounds with identical molecular formulae, but which nevertheless are not structural isomers, is explicable by the concept of geometric isomerism, which is one type of stereoisomerism. The simplest example of geometric isomerism occurs when a hydrogen atom attached to each carbon atom in ethylene is replaced by another atom or group. Compounds with these atoms or groups on opposite sides of the carbon–carbon double bond are termed *trans*; those in which they are on the same side are termed *cis*.

Isomerism is important for three main reasons: to classify organic compounds; as part of the structure-determining process for compounds of unknown structure; and because of its role in the properties of certain naturally-occurring substances. One example of the latter two categories is in the area of pest control.

The aphid alarm pheromone is *trans*-β-farnesene; the *cis* isomer is inactive. Use of this alarm pheromone would, in principle, allow much lower concentrations of conventional insecticides to be used for pest control.

SAQ 18 Draw out all the possible structures with molecular formula C_4H_8O that contain a hydroxyl group and a carbon–carbon double bond, and indicate which pairs are geometric isomers.

5 INTO THE THIRD DIMENSION—CHIRALITY

In the previous Section, you were introduced to one type of stereoisomerism, known as geometric isomerism. In this Section you will meet the phenomenon of **chirality** which gives rise to the other type of stereoisomerism, known as **optical isomerism**. This final type of isomerism has the most profound consequences for the chemistry of life, and the Section concludes with some examples of the effects of chirality in nature.

5.1 CHIRALITY AND THE TETRAHEDRAL CARBON ATOM

In Section 3.3 you discovered the phenomenon of structural isomerism: the existence of compounds that have the same molecular formula but with atoms connected in a different order. At that point we were not very much concerned with the detailed shape of molecules. Then, in Section 4.2, you discovered a type of isomerism, stereoisomerism, that does depend on the precise spatial disposition of atoms. At that point, we were concerned with the arrangement of atoms or groups around a carbon–carbon double bond, which would give rise to the type of stereoisomerism known as geometric isomerism. In that case, the six atoms closest to the double bond all lie in a plane. Now you are about to discover the second type of stereoisomerism, one that is perhaps more subtle to understand than the others, yet has profound consequences for the chemistry of life itself. The key to this type of isomerism is the spatial arrangement of atoms or groups around a *saturated* carbon atom. As with the other types of isomerism already discussed, this is introduced by means of an AV sequence.

You should now work through the third, and final, AV sequence for these two Units, entitled 'Chirality', which is on Tape 3 (Side 2, Band 2). It should take no more than 30 minutes in all. In addition to the Frames that follow, you will need to use your molecular model kit, your stereoviewer, filmstrip 2, a mirror, preferably at least 12 cm × 12 cm (or 12 cm in diameter if circular), and some means of holding it vertical on your work table. One possible way is to use the retort stand, boss and clamp from the Experiment Kit.

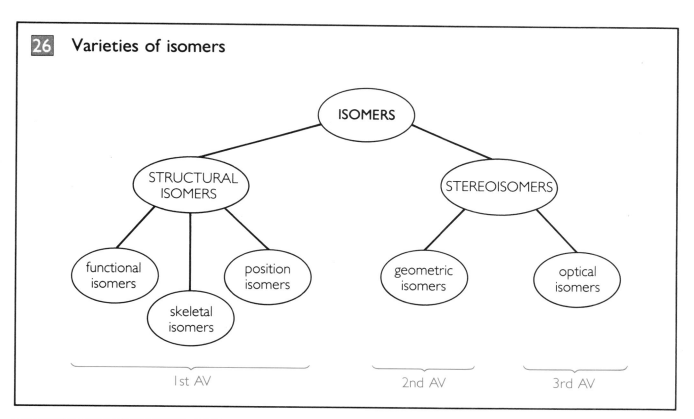

26 Varieties of isomers

27 Equivalent structural formulae

28 Optical isomerism

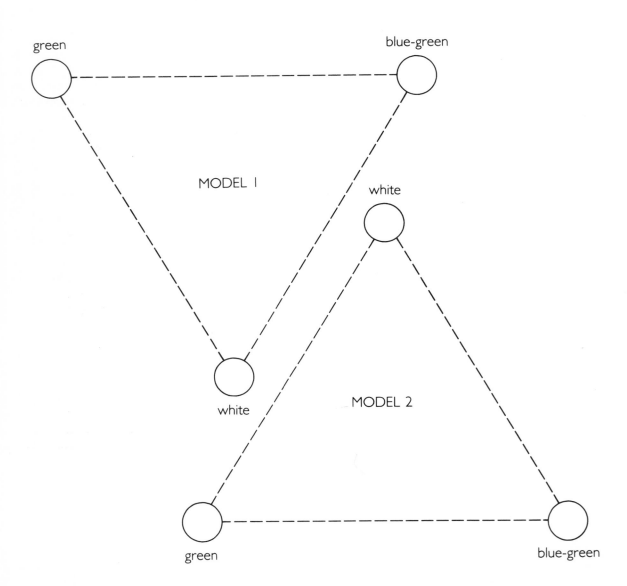

For structure (b):

- model 1 and model 2 are non-superimposable

- they are therefore *different* structures with the same formula

- the order of atoms is the same so they are not structural isomers

- they are therefore *stereoisomers* – called *optical isomers*

29 Chirality

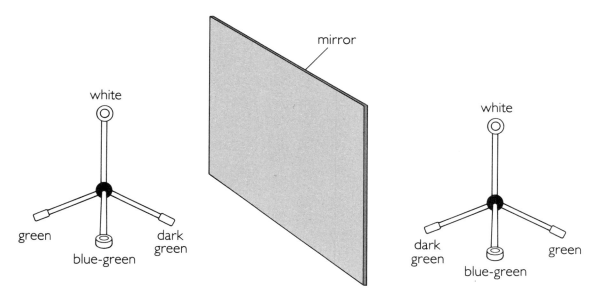

- One model is the mirror image of the other — related as a left hand and a right hand.

- They therefore have the property of 'handedness' or *chirality.*

- The two models are said to be *chiral.*

- One test for chirality: can a model of the molecule be superimposed on a model of its mirror image?

- A *chiral centre* is a carbon atom attached to *four* different atoms or groups.

- A second test for chirality: is there a chiral centre present in the molecule?

30 Chiral and non-chiral conformations

$$Br—\overset{\overset{\displaystyle H}{|}}{\underset{\underset{\displaystyle H}{|}}{C}}—\overset{\overset{\displaystyle H}{|}}{\underset{\underset{\displaystyle H}{|}}{C}}—Cl$$ 1-bromo-2-chloroethane

- Rotation can take place easily about carbon–carbon single bonds.

- Each different shape obtained is called a conformation.

- To be chiral, all possible conformations must be chiral — if there is one single conformation that is non-chiral, the molecule is non-chiral.

- Looking for a chiral centre avoids the need to consider different conformations.

31 Summary

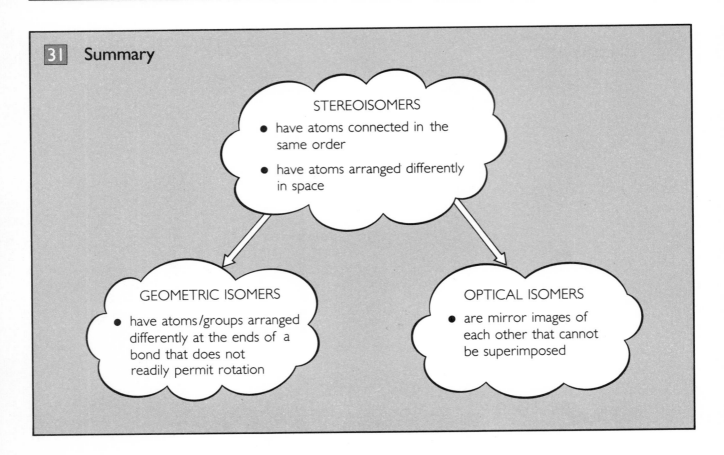

STEREOISOMERS

- have atoms connected in the same order
- have atoms arranged differently in space

GEOMETRIC ISOMERS

- have atoms/groups arranged differently at the ends of a bond that does not readily permit rotation

OPTICAL ISOMERS

- are mirror images of each other that cannot be superimposed

SAQ 19 Make models or three-dimensional drawings of the following molecules, and use the mirror-image test to decide which of the molecules is/are chiral.

(a) $CHBrF_2$

(b)
$$H-\overset{\overset{\displaystyle F}{|}}{\underset{\underset{\displaystyle Cl}{|}}{C}}-OH$$

(c) $BrCH_2-CHCl_2$

(d) $BrCH_2-CHBrCl$

SAQ 20 By looking for a chiral centre, decide which of the following molecules are chiral and which are non-chiral.

(a) CHI_3

(b) $CH_3-CHBrCl$

(c) $CH_3-CH_2-\overset{\overset{\displaystyle }{|}}{\underset{\underset{\displaystyle OH}{|}}{C}}H-CH_3$

(d) CHF_2-CH_2F

(e)
$$CH_3-\underset{\underset{\displaystyle OH}{|}}{C}H-\overset{\overset{\displaystyle O}{\parallel}}{C}\underset{\underset{\displaystyle OH}{\diagdown}}{{}}$$

(f) $CH_3-CH_2-\underset{\underset{\displaystyle CH_3}{|}}{C}H-CH_2-CH_2-CH_3$

PLANE-POLARIZED LIGHT

5.2 THE DETECTION AND OCCURRENCE OF CHIRALITY

You will recall from Sections 3 and 4 that the compounds that are structural isomers or geometric isomers have different properties one from another. For example, the structural isomers propan-1-ol and propan-2-ol have different boiling temperatures as do the geometric isomers *cis*-but-2-ene and *trans*-but-2-ene. But optical isomers, in many of their properties, appear to be identical! For example, the 'left-handed' form of butan-2-ol has exactly the same boiling temperature as the 'right-handed' form. Further, in many of their reactions, the 'left-handed' and 'right-handed' forms react to give the same products at the same rate. How, then, may optical isomers be distinguished, and indeed why are they so important?

The key to how we can distinguish optical isomers lies in their name—we use light. But it has to be a special type of light called **plane-polarized light**.

In Unit 10, you saw that light can be modelled as an electromagnetic wave in which the magnitudes of the (mutually perpendicular) electric and magnetic fields vary in a regular fashion (Figure 21). The oscillations in the electric or magnetic fields each take place in a plane at right-angles to the direction of propagation.

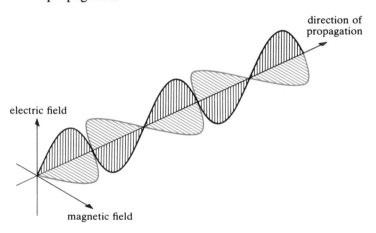

FIGURE 21 Light as an electromagnetic wave.

Let us concentrate on just one of these, say the oscillations in the electric field. In ordinary light, all possible orientations of the direction of these oscillations are present (Figure 22).

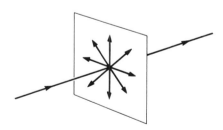

FIGURE 22 Unpolarized light, in which the directions of the oscillating electric (or magnetic) fields of the waves occur in all directions perpendicular to the direction of propagation of the light.

However, certain substances, known as polarizing materials, can reduce such light to a form in which the electric field oscillations take place only in one direction. One such material is 'Polaroid' sheet of the kind used in certain types of sunglasses. The direction of oscillation of the electric field and the direction of propagation of the light wave then lie in a single plane: the light is said to be plane-polarized (Figure 23). If now another piece of Polaroid sheet (another 'polarizer') is placed in the emerging beam, and is orientated in precisely the same way as the first, the light it transmits is unchanged: that is, it remains plane-polarized, and the brightness is undiminished. However, if the second piece is rotated through 90° so that the plane of polarization is orientated at right-angles to the first, then no light emerges from the end of the system; the polarizers are said to be 'crossed' (Figure 24). At intermediate orientations, the light intensity is reduced but not totally extinguished.

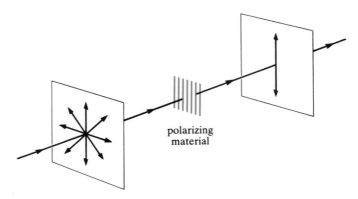

FIGURE 23 The production of plane-polarized light using a piece of polarizing material (Polaroid sheet).

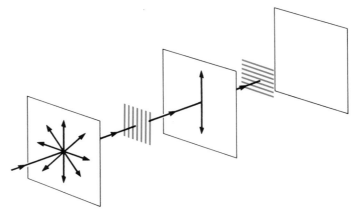

FIGURE 24 The extinction of light by two pieces of Polaroid sheet with their direction of polarization set at right-angles to each other.

Plate 6 shows just such an experimental arrangement. The components are, in order from the left-hand side, a sodium lamp, a piece of Polaroid sheet mounted in a holder, a cylindrical cell half-full of liquid, and finally a second piece of Polaroid sheet in its holder. This has a metal strip attached to allow rotation of the front polarizer: the two polarizers are 'crossed' when this is in a vertical position. In each case, the rear polarizer remains fixed in position; only the front one is rotated.

Plate 7a shows what happens when a chiral substance (usually in solution or as a liquid) is placed between the two polarizers. In this case the substance is a naturally-occurring liquid ketone called (+)carvone: the significance of the (+) will become clear in a moment. You can see that the yellow–orange light from the sodium lamp only passes through the liquid: no light is transmitted through the upper half of the cell (remember the cell is only half-full; the crescent of light results from some light being reflected from the inner surface of the bottom of the cylindrical cell). This is because *chiral substances rotate the plane of polarization of light passing through them.* Consequently, the plane of polarization of the front polarizer is no longer at right-angles to the plane of polarization of the light that has passed through the sample.

Now look at Plate 7b. Rotating the front polariser anticlockwise still allows the light to be transmitted through the liquid, but now light is also transmitted through the upper half of the cell as well, since the polarizers are no longer crossed. Now look at Plate 7c. This shows the effect of rotating the front polarizer clockwise by just the right amount to counteract the rotation of polarization brought about by the (+)carvone; now the light is no longer transmitted through the sample, but it *is* transmitted through the upper half of the cell. By convention, because the polarizer is rotated clockwise, this sample is given the designation (+); if the front polarizer had had to be rotated anticlockwise to achieve the same effect, the sample would have been designated (−)carvone. This is shown in Plates 8a–c, which show the analogous series of observations with a sample of (−)carvone in the cell.

Substances which rotate the plane of polarized light, such as (+)carvone and (−)carvone, are said to show **optical activity**. The amount that the polarizer has to be rotated is characteristic of the individual substance, and depends on the concentration of the sample and the length of the cell. For example, pure (+)carvone in a 10 cm path length cell (the arrangement in Plates 7a–c) rotates the plane of polarization through 60.4°, a value that is equal in magnitude, though opposite in sense (direction), to that produced by (−)carvone. This illustrates a general principle: *a chiral molecule and its optical isomer rotate the plane of polarization of polarized light by equal amounts but in opposite senses.*

The amount by which a given optical isomer rotates the plane of polarization is a characteristic signature of that compound. When measured under a standard set of conditions this quantity is termed its **specific rotation**. The specific rotation is most frequently determined using light from a sodium lamp, and is denoted $[\alpha]_D$: the D stands for the so-called D lines in the sodium atomic spectrum, which give rise to the characteristic colour of the sodium lamp. The specific rotation is defined by the following equation, where α is the angle that the front polarizer has to be rotated to prevent light transmission through the sample, c is the concentration in $g\,cm^{-3}$ and l is the path length of the cell in units of dm (10^{-1} m):

$$[\alpha]_D = \frac{\alpha}{lc}$$

Table 11 shows the values of the specific rotation* for some of the optical isomers you met in SAQ 20.

TABLE 11   Specific rotation of some chiral molecules

Name	Formula	$[\alpha]_D$†
(+)butan-2-ol	$CH_3-CH_2-\underset{\underset{\displaystyle OH}{\vert}}{CH}-CH_3$	+13.9°
(+)3-methylhexane	$CH_3-CH_2-\underset{\underset{\displaystyle CH_3}{\vert}}{CH}-CH_2-CH_2-CH_3$	+9.5°
(+)lactic acid	$CH_3-\underset{\underset{\displaystyle OH}{\vert}}{CH}-\underset{\overset{\displaystyle \vert\vert}{}}{C}-OH$ O	+3.8°

† The (−) isomer would have an equal value of $[\alpha]_D$, but with the opposite sign.

ITQ 6   What would be the rotation produced by a solution of (−)butan-2-ol with a concentration of $0.100\,g\,cm^{-3}$ and a path length of 0.100 dm? Would the front polarizer need to be rotated in a clockwise or an anticlockwise direction?

You may be wondering, if you were to make molecular models of the two mirror-image forms of, say, butan-2-ol, which would correspond to (+)butan-2-ol and which to (−)butan-2-ol. *There is no simple connection between the molecular 'handedness' of a particular optical isomer and the sign of optical rotation.* This has important and far-reaching ramifications, some of which will be apparent in a moment. In fact, the model shown in stereoslide 12 corresponds to (+)butan-2-ol and that in stereoslide 13 to (−)butan-2-ol, but it is by no means easy to establish that connection.

---

* For convenience, the values of specific rotation are always given in degrees, although (strictly) the units are degrees $cm^3\,g^{-1}\,dm^{-1}$.

Many naturally occurring chiral molecules are found in only *one* of the two mirror-image forms. One such group of compounds in which chirality is of particular importance are the naturally-occurring **amino acids**. Amino acids contain both an amino group, $-NH_2$, and a carboxyl group, $-\overset{\displaystyle O}{\underset{\displaystyle \parallel}{C}}-OH$.

They are building blocks of proteins and will be discussed at greater length in Section 7.5 and in Unit 22. In all, there are about 20 naturally occurring amino acids, and some of these are shown below.

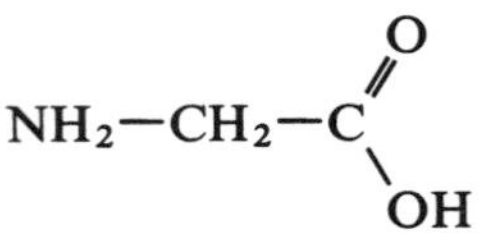

$$NH_2-CH_2-C\overset{\displaystyle O}{\diagdown}_{OH} \qquad \text{glycine}$$

$$NH_2-\underset{\underset{\displaystyle CH_3}{|}}{CH}-C\overset{\displaystyle O}{\diagdown}_{OH} \qquad \text{alanine}$$

$$NH_2-\underset{\underset{\displaystyle \underset{\displaystyle Ph}{|}}{\underset{\displaystyle CH_2}{|}}}{CH}-C\overset{\displaystyle O}{\diagdown}_{OH} \qquad \text{phenylalanine}$$

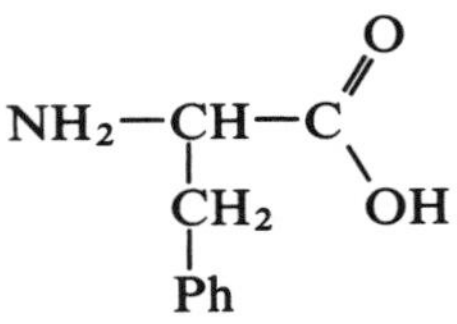

$$NH_2-\underset{\underset{\displaystyle \underset{\displaystyle OH}{|}}{\underset{\displaystyle CH_2}{|}}}{CH}-C\overset{\displaystyle O}{\diagdown}_{OH} \qquad \text{serine}$$

Look at the fomulae of glycine and alanine. By looking for a chiral centre, decide if either of these is chiral.

Glycine is non-chiral since neither carbon atom is attached to four different groups. Alanine, however, is chiral, since the central carbon is attached to four different groups, that is, $-NH_2$, $-H$, $-CH_3$ and $-\overset{\displaystyle }{\underset{\displaystyle O}{C}}-OH$. In fact,

all the other naturally-occurring amino acids are chiral also. The naturally-occurring isomers of the three chiral amino acids above are (+)alanine, (−)phenylalanine and (+)serine.

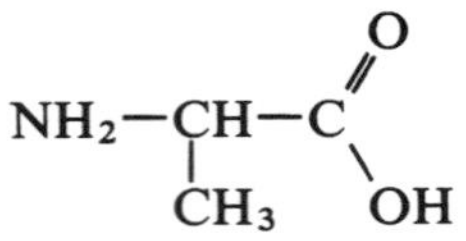

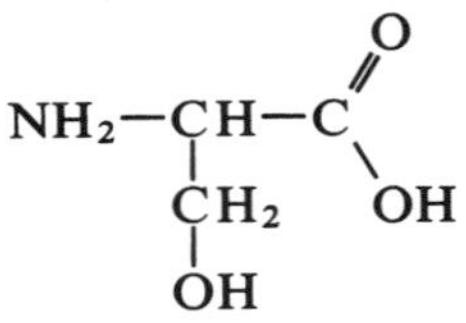

The fascinating point is that not only do they occur almost exclusively in one of the two possible chiral forms, but *they all have the same handedness*. All the amino acids have three groups in common:

$$-H, \ -NH_2 \ \text{and} \ -\overset{\displaystyle }{\underset{\displaystyle O}{C}}-OH,$$

which are attached to the central carbon atom. If you were to make a model in which these three groups were attached to a carbon atom, then, whatever the fourth group, all the commonly occurring amino acids would fit the chiral template shown in Figure 25a, and not the template shown in Figure 25b. They are said to have the same **configuration**. By convention, this is denoted by using a small capital L. Thus, all the natural amino acids have the L configuration. The unnatural isomers are said to have the D configuration, again by convention. D and L are used to describe the configuration of the molecule (from the Latin words *dexter* meaning 'right', and *laevus* meaning 'left'), whereas (+) and (−) are used to describe the effect on the plane of polarized light of a macroscopic sample of the two isomers. That is why the fact that there is no simple relationship between the two was stressed earlier: some natural amino acids are (+) and some (−) (see above), but they all have the L configuration, that is the same handedness.

This raises some intriguing questions. For instance:

How did it come about that we live in a world in which all the natural amino acids have the L configuration and not the D configuration?

If amino acids occur naturally elsewhere in the Universe, do they have the same configuration as those on Earth?

We shall pursue these questions further in Section 8.2 when we briefly consider the origin of chirality in natural substances.

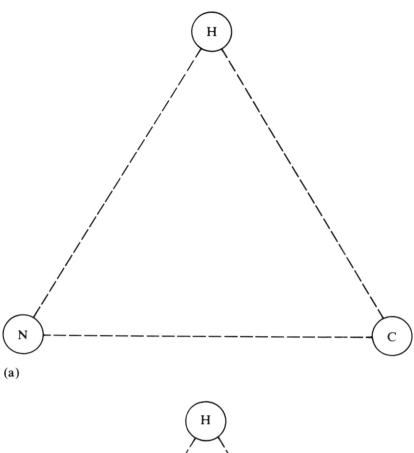

(a)

(b)

FIGURE 25 Chiral templates which fit only the natural (a) or unnatural (b) isomers of the 19 commonly-occurring chiral amino acids. These templates fit the models that you can make with your molecular model kit.

RACEMIC MIXTURE

ESTER

There is, however, one type of question that we are able to answer at this stage. Lewis Carroll put it in a nutshell in *Through the Looking-glass* (1872):

> "How would you like to live in Looking-glass house, Kitty? I wonder if they'd give you milk, there? Perhaps looking-glass milk isn't good to drink . . . ."

Milk contains a number of chiral substances, among which is 'milk sugar', (+)lactose. So 'looking-glass' milk presumably would contain (−)lactose, since (−)lactose is the mirror-image of (+)lactose. It is unlikely that 'looking-glass' milk would be harmful, but it would probably taste different and not be nutritious. It is for a similar reason that (−)glucose (the mirror image of natural (+)glucose) has been patented as a non-fattening sweetener: it is as sweet as (+)glucose but cannot be metabolized. By contrast, the natural (−)phenylalanine tastes bitter while the unnatural (+) isomer tastes sweet. Of the two forms of another amino acid, glutamic acid, only the natural isomer (as its sodium salt, monosodium glutamate, MSG) is an effective flavour-enhancing agent for meats, soups and other foods. And, (+)carvone and (−)carvone, though both occur naturally, one in caraway and the other in mint, do smell distinctly different, perhaps not surprisingly one of caraway seed and the other of mint. You will meet another example of a pair of optical isomers that can be distinguished biologically in the next Section, when we look at a chiral substance that is produced industrially for use in the pharmaceutical industry.

5.3 OPTICAL ISOMERS IN ACTION

We have seen in the previous Section that optical isomers have the following characteristics:

1 An optical isomer can only be distinguished from its mirror image form when in a chiral environment, such as that provided by plane-polarized light. The difference in taste between (+)phenylalanine and (−)phenylalanine or the difference in smell between (+)carvone and (−)carvone points to the presence of such an environment in living systems. These effects arise from the difference in the way a chiral molecule and its optical isomer interact with a chiral receptor site. This is analogous to the difference in 'fit' between a left hand and a right hand with a left glove (Figure 26) (hence the term 'handedness').

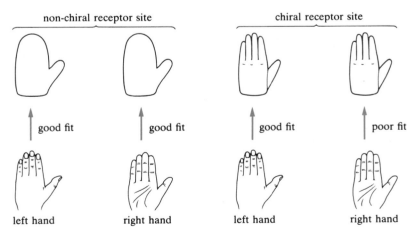

non-chiral receptor site   chiral receptor site

good fit   good fit   good fit   poor fit

left hand   right hand   left hand   right hand

FIGURE 26 Hand-and-glove analogy for the interaction between a chiral molecule and a chiral receptor site.

2 In the absence of such a chiral environment, optical isomers have identical physical properties: for example (+)butan-2-ol and (−)butan-2-ol have identical boiling temperatures, solubilities etc.

Consequently, when a potentially chiral compound is synthesized in the laboratory or industrially manufactured, unless some chiral agent is present, for example another chiral molecule, there is an equal probability of producing either isomer. The result is a 50 : 50 mixture of both isomers. This is called a **racemic mixture**.

What do you think the effect of a racemic mixture would be on the plane of polarized light?

The two isomers have an equal and opposite effect on polarized light: in a 50:50 mixture the effects would cancel and the net result would be zero rotation of the plane of polarized light. So a sample of racemic butan-2-ol, denoted ($\pm$)butan-2-ol, is said to be optically inactive, but samples of (+)butan-2-ol and (−)butan-2-ol, which contain just one isomer, are said to be optically active. Compounds that are non-chiral are also optically inactive, of course.

So, if a sample of just one optical isomer is needed, how can it be made? Is there any way in which optical isomers can be separated? The answer to the latter question is yes, and one of the methods that can be used is shown in the TV programme 'Organic molecules in action'. This involves the production of an **ester** called glycidyl butyrate. An ester is a class of compound containing the $C-O-\underset{\underset{O}{\|}}{C}-$ group*. Glycidyl butyrate has the formula shown below.

$$CH_2-CH-CH_2-O-\underset{\underset{O}{\|}}{C}-CH_2-CH_2-CH_3$$
$$\text{(epoxide ring at CH}_2\text{-CH)}$$

glycidyl butyrate

This compound has one feature that you have not met previously, a ring of atoms made up of two carbons and one oxygen. You will be able to see what this looks like shortly when you will be asked to make up a model. First, though, why is glycidyl butyrate of interest?

Until relatively recently, the majority of pharmaceutical products that have chiral molecules were produced as racemic mixtures. As pointed out in the previous Section, humans are made up of chiral substances and can often distinguish between optical isomers. As a consequence, only one isomer is likely to be beneficial; the other may be excreted unchanged, or potentially, it could have adverse side-effects. With the growing concern about ingesting substances unnecessarily, pharmaceutical companies are actively seeking ways of producing just the desired optical isomer. The use of glycidyl butyrate as a starting material is one possible method for the production of a family of drugs known as 'beta-blockers': these are used primarily to reduce blood pressure and to treat angina and other heart-related disorders† (Figure 27).

First, then, how is glycidyl butyrate made? To find out, we need to begin to examine the chemical properties of two functional groups, a story that will be taken up more comprehensively in the next Section.

Glycidyl butyrate is an ester. One method of forming esters is to heat together an alcohol and a carboxylic acid. For example, ethyl acetate can be produced from ethanol and acetic acid:

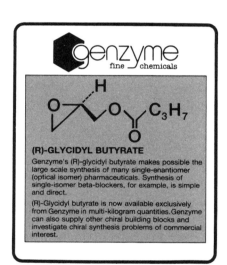

(R)-GLYCIDYL BUTYRATE

Genzyme's (R)-glycidyl butyrate makes possible the large scale synthesis of many single-enantiomer (optical isomer) pharmaceuticals. Synthesis of single-isomer beta-blockers, for example, is simple and direct.

(R)-Glycidyl butyrate is now available exclusively from Genzyme in multi-kilogram quantities. Genzyme can also supply other chiral building blocks and investigate chiral synthesis problems of commercial interest.

FIGURE 27 Glycidyl butyrate is a chiral compound with uses in the pharmaceutical industry for the production of chiral drugs, for example, 'beta-blockers'.

$$CH_3-CH_2-OH + CH_3-\underset{\underset{O}{\|}}{C}-OH \xrightarrow{H^+} CH_3-CH_2-O-\underset{\underset{O}{\|}}{C}-CH_3 + H_2O$$

ethanol
(alcohol)

acetic acid
(carboxylic acid)

ethyl acetate
(ester)

---

* Since the ester group is not symmetrical, formulae can be written with the carbonyl group either on the left $(-\underset{\underset{O}{\|}}{C}-O-C)$ or on the right $(C-O-\underset{\underset{O}{\|}}{C}-)$. In these Units you will find ester formulae written both ways.

† You will learn more of the workings of the heart and blood circulation and of the beta-blocker drug called propranolol in Unit 23.

ENZYME

But even if the reaction mixture is heated and a strong acid used as a catalyst (signified by the H^+ over the arrow), the reaction can be very slow. A way around this problem is first to convert the carboxylic acid into a more reactive form known as an acid chloride: this can be achieved using a reagent called thionyl chloride, $SOCl_2$. In the case of acetic acid, the reaction would give acetyl chloride:

$$CH_3-\underset{\underset{O}{\|}}{C}-OH + SOCl_2 \longrightarrow CH_3-\underset{\underset{O}{\|}}{C}-Cl + SO_2 + HCl$$

acetic acid   thionyl chloride   acetyl chloride
(carboxylic acid)   (acid chloride)

The acid chloride is much more reactive than the acid itself, and reaction with the alcohol rapidly gives the ester:

$$CH_3-CH_2-OH + CH_3-\underset{\underset{O}{\|}}{C}-Cl \longrightarrow CH_3-CH_2-O-\underset{\underset{O}{\|}}{C}-CH_3 + HCl$$

ITQ 7   Write down the two reactions involved if the same method were used to form glycidyl butyrate from the alcohol glycidol and butyric acid. (In doing so, concentrate on the functional groups involved.)

$$\overset{\overset{\displaystyle O}{\diagup\diagdown}}{CH_2-CH}-CH_2-OH \qquad\qquad CH_3-CH_2-CH_2-\underset{\underset{O}{\|}}{C}-OH$$

glycidol   butyric acid

In the manufacture of glycidyl butyrate, the glycidol and butyric acid are bought in from other suppliers: these compounds would have been manufactured by a series of reactions from compounds obtained initially by refining crude oil. The two stages involved in converting these starting compounds are shown in the TV programme 'Organic molecules in action'.

Stereoslides 16 and 17 show models of the glycidol molecule. Make up models identical to the two in the stereoslides. Then, by comparing them, decide whether or not glycidol is chiral.

The two models of the glycidol molecule cannot be superimposed: glycidol is chiral and the two models represent the two mirror-image forms, that is, the two optical isomers. (It is more difficult to determine this by looking for a chiral centre since the carbon atom concerned is part of the three-atom ring.) Since glycidol is chiral, glycidyl butyrate will also be chiral—simply attaching the non-chiral $CH_3-CH_2-CH_2-\underset{\underset{O}{\|}}{C}-O-$ group does not alter the mirror-image relationship of the two forms.

Do you expect the product glycidyl butyrate to be a racemic mixture or do you expect just one of the isomers to be formed?

On the basis of the earlier discussions, since no chiral environment is involved, the product is a racemic mixture. But it is only the $(-)$ isomer that is needed as a chemical intermediate: how then can this be obtained from the racemic mixture?

The answer is to make use of a naturally-occurring agent called an **enzyme**. (You will learn a great deal about enzymes in Unit 22.) For our purposes, you should think of it simply as a biological catalyst. Enzymes are made up largely of amino acids linked together in a chain, so they are chiral. One such enzyme, called lipase, has the ability to split up esters, such as glycidyl butyrate, into their constituent alcohol and acid. But because lipase is chiral, *only one of the optical isomers will react*, while the other remains essentially unaffected. In fact, it is the (+) isomer that is split up preferentially. The (−) isomer that is needed for the synthesis of the 'beta-blocker' drugs is left intact (stereoslide 18). This separation process is also shown in the TV programme.

☐ What measurement could be made to check that the separation had been successful?

■ The measurement of the rotation of plane-polarized light.

ITQ 8 Pure (−)glycidyl butyrate has a specific rotation of −29°. In the programme, an electronic instrument called a *polarimeter* was used to measure the rotation produced by the product ester. A value of −0.29° was found for a solution of concentration $0.10\,g\,cm^{-3}$ and with a path length of $0.10\,dm$. How successful has the separation process been?

So, by using an enzyme, optical isomers can be separated efficiently. However, such a process has an inherent disadvantage.

Can you suggest what this might be?

The problem is that half of the product is wasted. Because of this inherent disadvantage, there is increasing interest in the use of chiral reagents so that only the desired isomer is produced rather than a racemic mixture. But, whichever method is used, the aim is the same—to produce a compound in which the molecules are all of the same handedness.

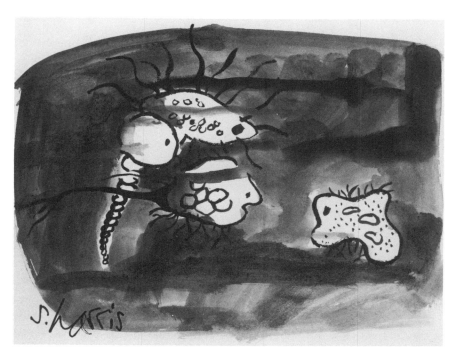

"THIS NEW DRUG WORKS ON STREPTOCOCCI, PNEUMOCOCCI AND STAPHYLOCOCCI. NOW HERE'S WHERE YOU COME IN...."

SUMMARY OF SECTION 5

The tetrahedral arrangement of atoms or groups around a saturated carbon atom can give rise to a new type of isomerism called optical isomerism. Optical isomerism is the second type of stereoisomerism. Optical isomers are molecules that can exist in two non-superimposable mirror image forms. Such molecules, which usually have four different groups attached to a saturated carbon atom, are called chiral.

Except when in a chiral environment, the two mirror-image forms (optical isomers) have identical properties. However, they can be distinguished by their effect on plane-polarized light (hence their name): by convention (+) isomers rotate the plane of polarized light clockwise, and (−) isomers rotate the plane of polarized light anticlockwise, the direction of rotation being determined from the viewpoint of the experimenter looking through the polarizers towards the light source. Each optical isomer rotates the plane of polarized light by a characteristic amount denoted by its specific rotation. In general, only one isomer occurs naturally, though occasionally both are found. An important group of naturally-occurring chiral compounds are the amino acids, the building blocks of proteins. The commonly occurring chiral amino acids are all of the same handedness; they are said to have the L configuration.

When a substance is synthesized in the laboratory or manufactured, unless some chiral agent is present both isomers are produced in equal numbers, giving a racemic mixture. Such mixtures (and compounds that are non-chiral) are optically inactive, whereas those in which there is just one isomer (or an excess of one isomer) are optically active. An example of this is the manufacture of (−)glycidyl butyrate, a starting material used for the manufacture of certain pharmaceutical products. The (−) isomer can be obtained from the initially produced racemic product using an enzyme. The efficiency of the process can be checked by measuring the optical rotation of the product.

SAQ 21   The ketone 4-methylheptan-3-one is the principal alarm pheromone of the leaf-cutting ant and is chiral. Identify the chiral centre, and say whether you think it possible that one optical isomer is more effective than the other as an alarm pheromone.

$$CH_3-CH_2-CH_2-\underset{\underset{CH_3}{|}}{CH}-\overset{\overset{O}{\|}}{C}-CH_2-CH_3$$

4-methylheptan-3-one

SAQ 22   Which of the following could, in principle, be correct experimental observations? Explain your answer in each case.

(a) (+)Serine is more soluble in water than (−)serine.

(b) Racemic butan-2-ol reacts with acetic acid to give as a product an ester that rotates the plane of polarized light clockwise.

(c) (+)Butan-2-ol reacts with acetic acid to give as a product an ester that rotates the plane of polarized light anticlockwise.

(d) (−)Methadone (a synthetic analgesic used for treating heroin addicts) is more effective than (+)methadone. (You may assume that the methadone molecule is chiral.)

(e) (+)4-Methylheptan-3-one (SAQ 21) boils at the same temperature as (−)4-methylheptan-3-one.

6 FUNCTIONAL GROUPS— CHEMICAL REACTIONS

Having completed our study of the structures of carbon compounds and their relationship to the phenomenon of isomerism, we now turn to the reactions of carbon compounds. To do this, we need to begin by re-examining the concepts of a functional group and of a homologous series, before going on to review the various functional groups that we have already met, and introduce some other important ones not yet covered.

6.1 CHEMICAL PROPERTIES OF HOMOLOGOUS SERIES

At the beginning of these two Units, we introduced the idea that organic molecules can be thought of as being made up of a (usually) inactive hydrocarbon part and one or more functional groups. We can see how that works in practice by taking as an example the ester-forming reactions used in the TV programme 'Organic molecules in action'. In Section 5.3, we used the example of the formation of ethyl acetate to introduce the manufacture of the slightly more complicated glycidyl butyrate. The two reactions involved were as follows. The first involved the use of thionyl chloride, $SOCl_2$, to form an acid chloride:

$$CH_3-\underset{\underset{O}{\|}}{C}-OH + SOCl_2 \longrightarrow CH_3-\underset{\underset{O}{\|}}{C}-Cl + SO_2 + HCl$$

acetic acid

$$CH_3-CH_2-CH_2-\underset{\underset{O}{\|}}{C}-OH + SOCl_2 \longrightarrow CH_3-CH_2-CH_2-\underset{\underset{O}{\|}}{C}-Cl + SO_2 + HCl$$

butyric acid

The second step then involved the reaction of the acid chloride with an alcohol:

$$CH_3-CH_2-OH + CH_3-\underset{\underset{O}{\|}}{C}-Cl \longrightarrow CH_3-CH_2-O-\underset{\underset{O}{\|}}{C}-CH_3 + HCl$$

ethanol   ethyl acetate

$$CH_2-CH-CH_2-OH + CH_3-CH_2-CH_2-\underset{\underset{O}{\|}}{C}-Cl \longrightarrow CH_2-CH-CH_2-O-\underset{\underset{O}{\|}}{C}-CH_2-CH_2-CH_3 + HCl$$

glycidol   glycidyl butyrate

We were able to do this because the first reaction only modified the carboxyl group in each case, and in the second reaction the $-\underset{\underset{O}{\|}}{C}-Cl$ group

reacted with the hydroxyl group of the alcohol. In neither reaction was the rest of the molecule affected, nor conversely did it affect the course of the reaction. However, the three-atom ring in glycidol is itself a functional group and, in principle, could have been affected by the conditions used. So for simplicity, let us concentrate on a series of related compounds containing a single functional group, the homologous series of linear alcohols.

☐ Can you recall how the members of a homologous series are related?

■ They differ from one another by one or more $-CH_2-$ groups.

We said in Section 5.3 that the direct reaction of an alcohol with a carboxylic acid is slow, even in some cases where a strong acid is added as a catalyst. That is why in the manufacture of glycidyl butyrate the two-step process outlined above was used. But in other instances, the direct reaction

67

is fast enough. We can write out this reaction for the three alcohols ethanol, propan-1-ol and butan-1-ol with acetic acid, as follows:

$$CH_3-CH_2-OH + CH_3-\underset{\underset{O}{\|}}{C}-OH \xrightarrow{\text{H}^+ \text{ catalyst}} CH_3-CH_2-O-\underset{\underset{O}{\|}}{C}-CH_3 + H_2O$$

ethyl acetate

$$CH_3-CH_2-CH_2-OH + CH_3-\underset{\underset{O}{\|}}{C}-OH \xrightarrow{\text{H}^+ \text{ catalyst}} CH_3-CH_2-CH_2-O-\underset{\underset{O}{\|}}{C}-CH_3 + H_2O$$

propyl acetate

$$CH_3-(CH_2)_2-CH_2-OH + CH_3-\underset{\underset{O}{\|}}{C}-OH \xrightarrow{\text{H}^+ \text{ catalyst}} CH_3-(CH_2)_2-CH_2-O-\underset{\underset{O}{\|}}{C}-CH_3 + H_2O$$

butyl acetate

See if you can write a general equation for this reaction.

One possibility is:

$$R-OH + CH_3-\underset{\underset{O}{\|}}{C}-OH \longrightarrow R-O-\underset{\underset{O}{\|}}{C}-CH_3 + H_2O$$

But we can go a stage further. The carboxylic acids form a homologous series themselves, of which acetic acid is just one member. So the reaction can be made even more general by writing it as follows, where R^1 represents one hydrocarbon group and R^2 is a second hydrocarbon group or a hydrogen atom:

$$\underset{\text{alcohol}}{R^1-OH} + \underset{\text{acid}}{R^2-\underset{\underset{O}{\|}}{C}-OH} \longrightarrow \underset{\text{ester}}{R^1-O-\underset{\underset{O}{\|}}{C}-R^2} + H_2O$$

☐ Why could R^1 not be a hydrogen atom?

■ In that case R^1-OH, would simply represent a water molecule, H_2O, not an alcohol molecule.

In fact, the above equation is not restricted to members of a particular homologous series: it implies that, whatever the identity of R^1 and R^2, the reaction will take place. The collection of all compounds with a given functional group is called a **class of compounds**. So, once more, chemists assert that, in the majority of cases at least, any alcohol (that is, any member of the alcohol class) will react with any carboxylic acid (that is, any member of the carboxylic acid class) to give the corresponding ester.

The general reaction scheme above simultaneously summarizes information concerning the many hundreds of alcohols and carboxylic acids that have been found to react in this way and predicts that the untold thousands which have not been tried will also react similarly. We can even say that for many other alcohols, for example, where R^1 may include other functional groups, the reaction is likely to take place (though the possibility of complications—other reactions taking place, for example—must always be borne in mind). This is so *because they each have the same functional group*. Perhaps you can now begin to perceive something of the usefulness of the fundamental division of a compound into an inactive hydrocarbon group and an active functional group that enables chemists to bring order into what would otherwise be a bewildering diversity of carbon compounds.

CLASS OF (ORGANIC)
COMPOUND

AMIDE

PEPTIDE BOND

6.2 THE VARIETY OF FUNCTIONAL GROUPS

In Section 6.1 we concentrated on the reaction of a carboxylic acid molecule with an alcohol molecule to form an ester.

☐ Write down and name the functional group in each of these three types of molecule.

■ The carboxylic acid functional group is $-\underset{\underset{O}{\|}}{C}-OH$, called the carboxyl group; the characteristic functional group of an alcohol is $-OH$, called the hydroxyl group; and the ester functional group is $-\underset{\underset{O}{\|}}{C}-O-C$, usually just called the ester group.

In this Section, we shall first review the other functional groups that have been discussed so far, and introduce one or two new ones. Then we shall go on, in Section 6.3, to look at just a few of the reactions that they undergo.

There is a wide variety of functional groups and an even greater variety of possible reactions from which to choose: the ones that we have selected are those which are of greatest importance both for industrial aspects of organic chemistry, for example in the manufacture of plastics, to be discussed in Section 7, and for biological processes, particularly the biochemistry discussed in Unit 22.

ITQ 9 You have already met most of the functional groups that we shall be studying in this Section. Try to write down from memory the functional groups in the following types of molecule: alkenes, alkynes, fluoroalkanes, aldehydes and ketones.

[handwritten margin notes:]
alkenes > C=C
alkynes > C≡C
fluoroalkanes > C−F
aldehydes −CH=O
Ketones C−C−C with ‖ O

The other functional groups that you have met so far are the $C-O-C$ group in ethers, the $-NH_2$ group in alkylamines and the $-\underset{\underset{O}{\|}}{C}-Cl$ group in acid chlorides. There is just one other functional group that has yet to be introduced and this is found in the group of compounds called **amides**. The characteristic functional group of an amide is $-\underset{\underset{O}{\|}}{C}-N\diagup$. As you will learn in the next Section, this is of key importance in biochemistry, because amino acids are linked together by amide links in the formation of proteins:*

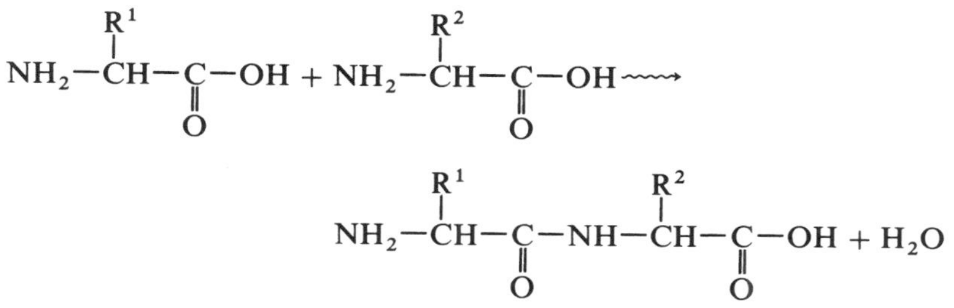

$$NH_2-\underset{R^1}{\overset{}{\underset{}{C}H}}-\underset{\underset{O}{\|}}{C}-OH + NH_2-\underset{R^2}{\overset{}{\underset{}{C}H}}-\underset{\underset{O}{\|}}{C}-OH \rightsquigarrow$$

$$NH_2-\underset{R^1}{\overset{}{\underset{}{C}H}}-\underset{\underset{O}{\|}}{C}-NH-\underset{R^2}{\overset{}{\underset{}{C}H}}-\underset{\underset{O}{\|}}{C}-OH + H_2O$$

This linkage between amino acids is so important that biochemists give it a special name: it is called a **peptide bond**.

The various functional groups are summarized in Table 12: we shall now go on to look at a selection of their more important reactions.

* The wavy arrow signifies that more than one reaction is needed to form an amide link from a carboxylic acid and an amine.

TABLE 12 Some common functional groups

Group	Class of compound	Example	
		Formula	Name
C—OH	alcohol (alkanol)	$\overset{3}{C}H_3-\overset{2}{C}H_2-\overset{1}{C}H_2-OH$	propan-1-ol
—CH=O	aldehyde (alkanal)	$CH_3-CH_2-CH=O$	propanal
$\underset{\parallel}{\overset{}{C}}-\underset{O}{\overset{}{C}}-C$	ketone (alkanone)	$\overset{4}{C}H_3-\overset{3}{C}H_2-\underset{O}{\overset{2}{C}}-\overset{1}{C}H_3$	butan-2-one
$-\underset{O}{\overset{\parallel}{C}}-OH$	carboxylic acid (alkanoic acid)	$CH_3-(CH_2)_4-\underset{O}{\overset{\parallel}{C}}-OH$	hexanoic acid
$-\underset{O}{\overset{\parallel}{C}}-O-C$	ester	$CH_3-\underset{O}{\overset{\parallel}{C}}-O-CH_2-CH_2-CH_3$	propyl acetate
$-\underset{O}{\overset{\parallel}{C}}-Cl$	acid chloride	$CH_3-CH_2-\underset{O}{\overset{\parallel}{C}}-Cl$	propanoyl chloride
$-\underset{O}{\overset{\parallel}{C}}-N\diagdown$	amide	$CH_3-\underset{O}{\overset{\parallel}{C}}-NH_2$	acetamide
C—O—C	ether	$CH_3-O-CH_2-CH_3$	methoxyethane
C—Hal*	haloalkane	$\overset{4}{C}H_3-\overset{3}{C}H_2-\overset{2}{C}H_2-\overset{1}{C}H_2-Cl$	1-chlorobutane
C—NH$_2$	alkylamine (alkanamine)	$\overset{3}{C}H_3-\underset{NH_2}{\overset{2}{C}H}-\overset{1}{C}H_3$	2-aminopropane

* Hal represents a halogen atom, that is, a fluorine, chlorine, bromine, or iodine atom (F, Cl, Br or I).

6.3 FUNCTIONAL GROUP TRANSFORMATIONS

In this Section, we shall find that, just as compounds can be classified according to their structure, so also can reactions be categorized by type. We shall concentrate on five different types of reaction organized into three groups: oxidation and reduction; addition; and condensation and hydrolysis.

Oxidation and reduction

As you might expect, the term **oxidation** is derived from reactions involving oxygen. Perhaps the most familiar example is one that car-owners could well do without—the rusting of iron. A similar change can be brought about by heating iron metal, Fe, in air, when the product is iron(III) oxide, Fe_2O_3:

$$4Fe + 3O_2 = 2Fe_2O_3$$

The oxidation is easily recognized by the fact that the original substance, Fe, has gained some oxygen atoms to form Fe_2O_3. So one definition of oxidation is the addition of oxygen to a substance. Another example of oxidation is a reaction you have carried out yourself: the conversion of red copper(I) oxide to black copper(II) oxide by heating in air:

$$2Cu_2O + O_2 = 4CuO$$

OXIDATION

REDUCTION

In this case, it is a little more difficult to see that oxygen has been added; however if you concentrate on the proportion of oxygen in the compound, it has clearly increased. If we now consider what has happened at the atomic level, it is apparent that copper(I) (that is, Cu^+) has been changed to copper(II) (that is, Cu^{2+}), a process that requires the *loss* of an electron.

So we have another definition of oxidation: a substance is oxidized if it loses electrons.

Processes which involve the *loss* of oxygen or the *gain* of electrons, that is, the opposite of oxidation, are called **reduction** reactions. For example, the reaction of hydrogen gas, H_2, with iron(III) oxide to produce iron metal is a reduction:

$$Fe_2O_3 + 3H_2 = 2Fe + 3H_2O$$

In this reaction, the Fe_2O_3 is reduced back to iron metal, but at the same time the hydrogen reacts to form water. Since this involves the gain of oxygen atoms, the hydrogen is being oxidized. This demonstrates another important point: any oxidation process is always accompanied by a corresponding reduction process, and vice versa. A further point is that this reduction is brought about by reaction with a hydrogen molecule; here the hydrogen ends up in a molecule of water, but often the hydrogen atoms become attached to the molecule being reduced. By extension, then, as well as involving removal of oxygen and/or addition of electrons, reduction can involve the addition of hydrogen. Conversely, as well as involving addition of oxygen and/or removal of electrons, oxidation can involve the removal of hydrogen.

One example of oxidation of an organic compound that many people are familiar with is the reaction that takes place if wine is left open to the air for too long, or sometimes if an unopened bottle is kept too long or the cork is faulty. A taste is all that is required to detect the conversion of the alcohol (ethanol) to vinegar (acetic acid). The production of wine vinegar involves just this process, the transformation being induced by the addition of *Acetobacter* bacteria.

$$CH_3-CH_2-OH + O_2 \xrightarrow{\text{\textit{Acetobacter}}} CH_3-\underset{\overset{\|}{O}}{C}-OH + H_2O$$

☐ Which definition of oxidation is appropriate to this transformation?

■ Either removal of hydrogen or addition of oxygen since both have taken place.

This same oxidation can be brought about in the laboratory by a variety of chemical reagents,* such as a solution of potassium dichromate, $K_2Cr_2O_7$(aq), in the presence of a strong acid such as dilute sulphuric acid, H_2SO_4(aq).

Now organic chemists are not always too concerned with what happens to a reagent in a reaction; they are much more concerned with the changes taking place to the carbon compound. So, for convenience and clarity, they often write the transformation as a (frequently unbalanced) reaction scheme. For example, the oxidation of ethanol to acetic acid would be written as follows:

$$CH_3-CH_2-OH + [O] \longrightarrow CH_3-\underset{\overset{\|}{O}}{C}-OH + H_2O$$

There are two things to note about this scheme. First, we denote the oxidizing agent as [O], which just signifies a source of oxygen without being specific. Secondly, because it is not a balanced equation (the oxygen is not present as oxygen atoms), an arrow is used rather than an equals sign.

* A reagent is simply a substance used to bring about a particular reaction.

PRIMARY ALCOHOL

SECONDARY ALCOHOL

TERTIARY ALCOHOL

ADDITION REACTION

The oxidation of ethanol, if carried out with care, can be made to proceed just part way to give acetaldehyde, $CH_3—CH=O$; this in turn can then be oxidized further to give acetic acid:

$$CH_3—CH_2—OH + [O] \longrightarrow CH_3—CH=O + H_2O$$

$$CH_3—CH=O + [O] \longrightarrow CH_3—\underset{\underset{O}{\|}}{C}—OH$$

In practice, stopping the oxidation at the aldehyde stage is often rather difficult, so the preparation of an aldehyde requires special care.

☐ Write generalized reaction schemes for the two oxidations shown above, using R— to represent a hydrocarbon group.

■ The first step is

$$R—CH_2—OH + [O] \rightarrow R—CH=O + H_2O$$

The second step is

$$R—CH=O + [O] \longrightarrow R—\underset{\underset{O}{\|}}{C}—OH$$

Note that the general formula for the alcohol is written $R—CH_2—OH$ *not* $R—OH$; that is because in this case the terminal carbon atom is itself directly involved in the reaction.

Not all alcohols can be oxidized to give carboxylic acids. For example, though propan-1-ol, $CH_3—CH_2—CH_2—OH$, can be oxidized to a carboxylic acid, namely propanoic acid, $CH_3—CH_2—\underset{\underset{O}{\|}}{C}—OH$, propan-2-ol,

$CH_3—\underset{\underset{OH}{|}}{CH}—CH_3$, cannot be oxidized further than acetone, $CH_3—\underset{\underset{O}{\|}}{C}—CH_3$.

☐ By carefully examining the changes that take place when ethanol is oxidized to acetic acid, can you suggest a reason for this?

■ The formation of a carboxylic acid from any alcohol involves the replacement of two hydrogen atoms on the carbon atom next to the hydroxyl group by an oxygen atom. In propan-2-ol there is only one such hydrogen atom, the other being a carbon atom.

Alcohols are called **primary**, **secondary** or **tertiary**, depending on the type of carbon to which the —OH group is attached: in primary alcohols, the carbon atom bearing the —OH group has *one* carbon atom attached; in secondary alcohols it has *two* carbon atoms attached; and in tertiary alcohols, there are *three* carbon atoms attached.

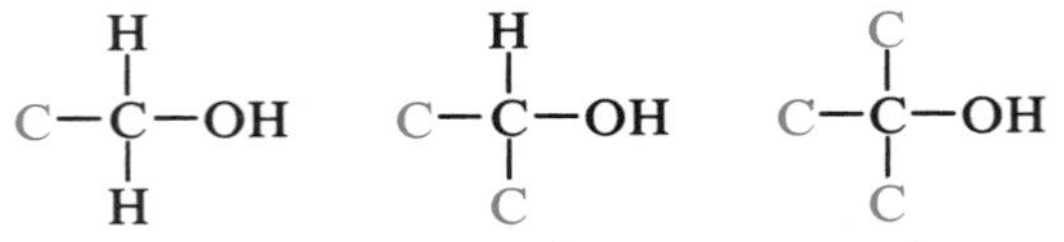

$$
\begin{array}{ccc}
\overset{\overset{H}{|}}{\underset{\underset{H}{|}}{C—C}}—OH & \overset{\overset{H}{|}}{\underset{\underset{C}{|}}{C—C}}—OH & \overset{\overset{C}{|}}{\underset{\underset{C}{|}}{C—C}}—OH \\
\text{primary} & \text{secondary} & \text{tertiary}
\end{array}
$$

Only primary alcohols give aldehydes, which can be further oxidized to carboxylic acids. Secondary alcohols give ketones on oxidation, which cannot easily be oxidized further; tertiary alcohols do not react at all.

ITQ 10 Classify the following four alcohols as primary, secondary, or tertiary.

$$CH_3-CH_2-CH_2-CH_2-OH$$
butan-1-ol

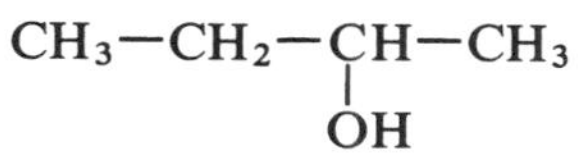

$$CH_3-CH_2-\underset{\underset{OH}{|}}{CH}-CH_3$$
butan-2-ol

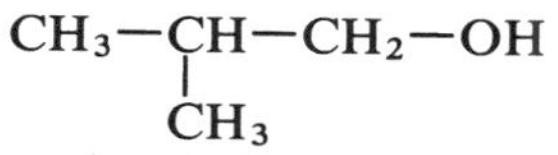

$$CH_3-\underset{\underset{CH_3}{|}}{CH}-CH_2-OH$$
2-methylpropan-1-ol

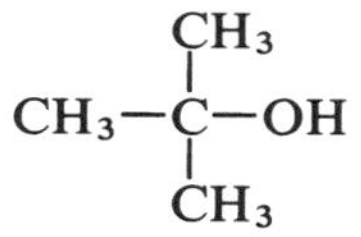

$$CH_3-\underset{\underset{CH_3}{|}}{\overset{\overset{CH_3}{|}}{C}}-OH$$
2-methylpropan-2-ol

Aldehydes and ketones can be readily converted back to alcohols.

☐ Can you recall what type of reaction this would involve?

■ It is the reverse of oxidation, that is reduction.

There are many reagents that will bring this about; two of the most common are sodium borohydride, $NaBH_4$, and hydrogen gas in the presence of a catalyst:

$$R-CH=O \xrightarrow[\text{H}_2\text{/catalyst}]{\text{NaBH}_4 \text{ or}} R-CH_2-OH$$

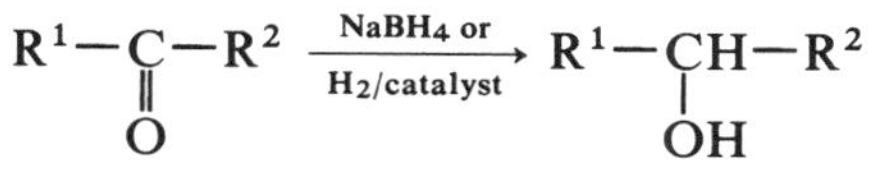

$$R^1-\underset{\underset{O}{\|}}{C}-R^2 \xrightarrow[\text{H}_2\text{/catalyst}]{\text{NaBH}_4 \text{ or}} R^1-\underset{\underset{OH}{|}}{CH}-R^2$$

Alkenes and alkynes can also be reduced using hydrogen gas and a catalyst.

$$\underset{R^2}{\overset{R^1}{\diagdown}}C=C\underset{R^4}{\overset{R^3}{\diagup}} \xrightarrow{\text{H}_2\text{/catalyst}} H-\underset{\underset{R^2}{|}}{\overset{\overset{R^1}{|}}{C}}-\underset{\underset{R^4}{|}}{\overset{\overset{R^3}{|}}{C}}-H$$

$$R^1-C\equiv C-R^2 \xrightarrow{\text{H}_2\text{/catalyst}} \underset{H}{\overset{R^1}{\diagdown}}C=C\underset{H}{\overset{R^2}{\diagup}}$$

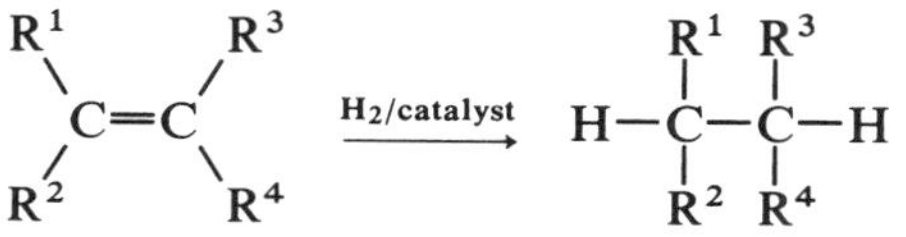

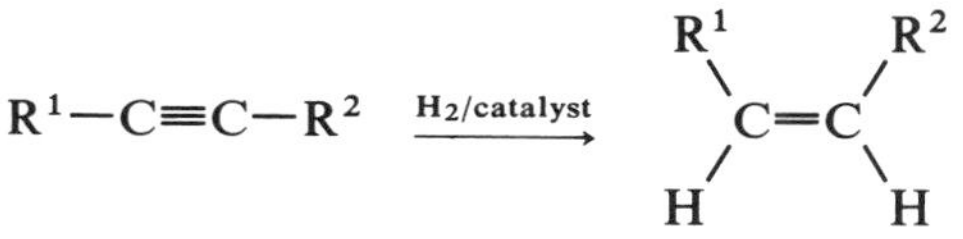

☐ Look at the product from reaction of the alkyne. Is this a *cis-* or a *trans*-alkene?

■ The product shown is a *cis*-alkene (the two hydrogen atoms adjacent to the double bond are on the same side).

Because of the way in which reduction by hydrogen and a catalyst takes place, the product alkene formed is only the *cis* isomer. The *trans* isomer alone can be obtained by use of the rather fearsome reagent, sodium metal in liquid ammonia.

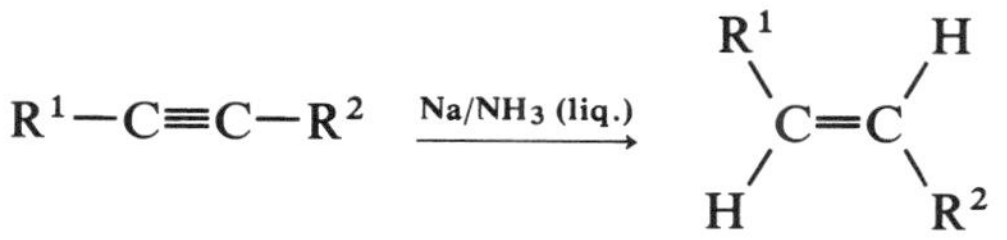

$$R^1-C\equiv C-R^2 \xrightarrow{\text{Na/NH}_3 \text{ (liq.)}} \underset{H}{\overset{R^1}{\diagdown}}C=C\underset{R^2}{\overset{H}{\diagup}}$$

The alkene obtained by reduction using hydrogen gas and a catalyst can undergo further reduction to give an alkane so, as with the oxidation of primary alcohols to aldehydes, care must be taken if the initially-formed product, in this case the alkene, is wanted.

Addition reactions

Reduction of double or triple bonds is an example of an **addition reaction**; these reactions involve the addition of extra atoms or groups to a multiple bond to form new single bonds. Another important example of an addition

CONDENSATION REACTION

HYDROLYSIS

reaction is the addition of bromine, Br_2, to an alkene; the disappearance of the orange-brown bromine colour is often used as a test for alkenes:

$$\underset{\substack{\text{alkene} \\ \text{(colourless)}}}{\overset{\displaystyle R^1 \qquad R^3}{\underset{\displaystyle R^2 \qquad R^4}{C=C}}} + \underset{\substack{\text{bromine} \\ \text{(orange-brown)}}}{Br_2} \longrightarrow \underset{\substack{\text{dibromoalkane} \\ \text{(colourless)}}}{\overset{\displaystyle R^1 \; R^3}{\underset{\displaystyle R^2 \; R^4}{Br-C-C-Br}}}$$

As you will see, addition reactions are very important in the formation of certain types of plastics (Section 7.1).

Condensation reactions and hydrolysis

The formation of esters from alcohols and carboxylic acids described in Section 6.1 is an example of a **condensation reaction**. Condensation reactions involve the joining together of two (or more) molecules, often with the expulsion of a small molecule such as H_2O, HCl or NH_3. As you may recall from Section 5, ester formation is often rather slow. A better method is first to convert the acid into an acid chloride, using thionyl chloride, $SOCl_2$:

$$R^1-\underset{\underset{\displaystyle O}{\|}}{C}-OH + \underset{\substack{\text{thionyl} \\ \text{chloride}}}{SOCl_2} \longrightarrow \underset{\text{acid chloride}}{R^1-\underset{\underset{\displaystyle O}{\|}}{C}-Cl} + HCl + SO_2$$

$$R^1-\underset{\underset{\displaystyle O}{\|}}{C}-Cl + R^2-OH \longrightarrow R^1-\underset{\underset{\displaystyle O}{\|}}{C}-O-R^2 + HCl$$

Acid chlorides are often used to form amides by reaction with amines:

$$R^1-\underset{\underset{\displaystyle O}{\|}}{C}-Cl + R^2-NH_2 \longrightarrow R^1-\underset{\underset{\displaystyle O}{\|}}{C}-NH-R^2 + HCl$$

☐ Is this a condensation reaction?

■ Yes, since it involves the linking together of two molecules with the expulsion of a small molecule, in this case HCl.

If a carboxylic acid reacts with an amine, the initial product is not an amide but something else.

☐ Can you guess what that might be, given that amines are (weak) bases?

■ The reaction of an acid and a base gives a salt, so this is most likely to be the initial product.

The amine accepts a hydrogen ion from the carboxylic acid to form a salt:

$$R^1-\underset{\underset{\displaystyle O}{\|}}{C}-OH + R^2-NH_2 \longrightarrow R^2-NH_3^+ \; {}^-O-\underset{\underset{\displaystyle O}{\|}}{C}-R^1$$

However, if the salt is then heated, usually to around 180°C or more in the absence of oxygen to prevent unwanted oxidation reactions, a water molecule is expelled and an amide formed:

$$R^2-NH_3^+ \; {}^-O-\underset{\underset{\displaystyle O}{\|}}{C}-R^1 \xrightarrow[\text{180°C}]{\text{heat}} R^2-NH-\underset{\underset{\displaystyle O}{\|}}{C}-R^1 + H_2O$$

The formation of amide links is of immense importance in the formation both of manufactured and of natural macromolecules (very long molecules) such as nylon or proteins. These are discussed in more detail in Section 7.

Units 17–18   The chemistry of carbon compounds

1   Introduction to the chemistry of carbon compounds
2   Characteristics of carbon compounds

The first part of these two Units that requires careful study is Section 2.1. Here, you get the 'pay-off' for mastering the theories of chemical bonding developed earlier in the Course, especially on covalent bonding, as this Section is simply an application of these theories to a particular group of substances. Section 2.2 is also important and should be studied carefully while Section 2.3, on halocarbons, can be read quickly as illustration and reinforcement of ideas in Section 2.2.

3   Families of compounds— catenation

Section 3 is very important. Sections 3.1 and 3.2, which introduce homologous series and the physical properties of such series, are fairly easy reading whereas the concept of structural isomerism, introduced in Section 3.3, is trickier to master. You should work through the AV sequence carefully. It may look time-consuming but is worth the investment of time as this concept is more easily understood when represented three-dimensionally.

4   Double and triple bonds— unsaturation

Section 4 is also important. Unsaturation, Section 4.1, and its associated isomerism, Section 4.2, needs to be understood. Take time to work through the second AV sequence which will give you some practice and help you to appreciate geometric isomerism. Section 4.3 may be read quickly as illustrative material. The details of the structural formulae and associated chemical names in Section 4.3 need *not* be remembered.

5   Into the third dimension— chirality

The important aspect to master is the concept of chirality, Section 5.1, and the AV sequence will help you here. Take time to work through it. Understanding the way in which it is detected, Section 5.2, is not so critical and may be studied less rigorously. Section 5.3 gives illustrative examples of the way in which different isomers can have different effects and shows why this type of isomerism is significant. It can be read quickly. You do *not* need to remember structures and names.

6   Functional groups— chemical reactions

Section 6 should be studied carefully since it contains core material on the chemical reactions of carbon-based molecules. You should familiarize yourself with the concept of a functional group, the 'business end' of a molecule, and try, for each different type of reaction, to focus your attention on what is happening to the functional group, giving less significance to the rest of a particular molecule.

7   Up the scale—giant molecules

Section 7 contains no new chemical concepts but applies what you have learnt earlier in these Units to very large molecules. You need to study it carefully since mastering this Section will provide a sound basis for your study of some of the concepts introduced in the biology Units. As you work through the Section, focus again on the behaviour of the functional groups in the molecules. This should help to make the task of understanding the reactions of these big molecules more manageable.

8   Into the past—prebiotic chemistry

Finally, Section 8 introduces some fascinating ideas but is not fundamental to an understanding of Units 17–18 and may be read through quickly.

SUP 26791 7

Printed by Hensal Press Ltd.

Another reaction of considerable importance in nature is the reverse of a condensation reaction in which the elements of a water molecule are added and the amide (or ester) link is broken. This type of reaction is called **hydrolysis**—literally, breaking down (lysis) with water. In the laboratory, this needs heat and a catalyst; in nature, it simply requires an enzyme:

$$R^2-O-\underset{\underset{O}{\|}}{C}-R^1 \xrightarrow[\text{catalyst}]{H_2O} R^2-OH + R^1-\underset{\underset{O}{\|}}{C}-OH$$

These then are a few of the many hundreds, if not thousands, of reactions involving carbon compounds that are known. The ones we have chosen are those of particular relevance to applications to be described in the next Section and to the biological chemistry to come in Units 22 to 24. But though we have only dealt with a small number, the immense variety of structures found in carbon compounds means that you are now in a position to predict the products from reactions involving literally hundreds of different substances. Such is the power of the concept of the functional group.

SUMMARY OF SECTION 6

The fact that members of a homologous series undergo similar chemical reactions is the basis for the fundamental distinction made by chemists between an active part of a molecule, the functional group, and an inactive part. Chemists go further and assert that any compound with a particular functional group will undergo characteristic chemical reactions. This idea was explored using as an example the formation of esters from alcohols and carboxylic acids.

There is a wide variety of functional groups, and each gives rise to its own class of compounds. The types of compound chosen for consideration in these Units are mainly those of particular importance in the manufacture of plastics and in biochemistry.

A selection of reactions involving these functional groups were considered. Oxidation is defined as the addition of oxygen, the loss of electrons or the removal of hydrogen; reduction, the converse of oxidation, is the removal of oxygen, the gain of electrons or the addition of hydrogen.

The product obtained from the oxidation of an alcohol depends on its structure: primary alcohols give aldehydes initially, further oxidation giving carboxylic acids; secondary alcohols give ketones; tertiary alcohols do not react.

Reduction of aldehydes and ketones give alcohols. Alkenes can also be reduced, to give alkanes, and alkynes on reduction give alkenes initially, and on further reduction give alkanes.

Addition reactions involve the addition of extra atoms or groups to a multiple bond to form new single bonds.

Condensation reactions involve the joining together of two (or more) molecules, often with the expulsion of a small molecule such as H_2O or HCl. Important examples are the reaction of a carboxylic acid or acid chloride with an alcohol to give an ester or with an amine to give an amide. Condensation reactions are of particular importance in the formation of manufactured and natural macromolecules.

Hydrolysis, the converse of condensation, in which a molecule of water brings about the cleavage of an ester or an amide, is of great importance in biochemistry.

SAQ 23 Classify each of the reactions 1–6 below as:

A oxidation;
B reduction;
C addition;
D condensation;
E hydrolysis.

C   1 $CH_3-CH=CH-CH_3 + HBr \longrightarrow CH_3-CH_2-CHBr-CH_3$

D   2 $CH_3-\overset{\underset{\|}{O}}{C}-Cl + CH_3-CH_2-NH-CH_3 \longrightarrow CH_3-\overset{\underset{\|}{O}}{C}-\overset{\underset{|}{CH_3}}{N}-CH_2-CH_3 + HCl$

A   3 $CH_3-\overset{\underset{|}{CH_3}}{CH}-CH_2-OH \xrightarrow{KMnO_4} CH_3-\overset{\underset{|}{CH_3}}{CH}-\overset{\underset{\|}{O}}{C}-OH$

B   4 $CH_3-CH_2-C{\equiv}CH \xrightarrow{H_2/catalyst} CH_3-CH_2-CH_2-CH_3$

D   5 $CH_2=CH-\overset{\underset{\|}{O}}{C}-OH + CH_3-OH \xrightarrow[heat]{H^+} CH_2=CH-\overset{\underset{\|}{O}}{C}-O-CH_3 + H_2O$

E   6 $CH_3-\overset{\underset{\|}{O}}{C}-NH-CH_2-CH_3 \xrightarrow{NaOH(aq)} CH_3-\overset{\underset{\|}{O}}{C}-O^-Na^+ + CH_3-CH_2-NH_2$

SAQ 24 For each of the reactions 1–4, choose which is the expected product from the three possibilities (a), (b) or (c) in each case.

1
$$CH_3-\underset{\underset{\displaystyle O}{\|}}{\underset{\displaystyle C}{\overset{\overset{\displaystyle CH_3}{|}}{CH}}}-CH_3 \xrightarrow{\text{NaBH}_4} \text{product}$$

2   $CH_3-C\equiv C-CH_2-CH_3 \xrightarrow{\text{Na/NH}_3\text{(liq)}} \text{product}$

3
$$CH_3-\underset{\underset{\displaystyle CH_3}{|}}{CH}-OH + CH_3-\underset{\underset{\displaystyle O}{\|}}{C}-Cl \longrightarrow \text{product}$$

4
$$\underset{\underset{\displaystyle CH_2-CH_2}{}}{\overset{\overset{\displaystyle CH_2}{}}{CH_2}}CH-CH_2-OH \xrightarrow{\text{K}_2\text{Cr}_2\text{O}_7} \text{product}$$

Reaction 1

$$CH_3-\underset{\underset{\displaystyle CH_3}{|}}{C}=CH-CH_3 \qquad CH_3-\underset{\underset{\displaystyle CH_3}{|}}{CH}-CH-OH \qquad CH_3-\underset{\underset{\displaystyle OH}{|}}{\overset{\overset{\displaystyle CH_3}{|}}{C}}-CH_2-CH_3$$

(a)   (b)   (c)

Reaction 2

$$\underset{\underset{\displaystyle CH_2-CH_3}{H}}{\overset{\overset{\displaystyle CH_3}{H}}{C}}=C \qquad \underset{\underset{\displaystyle H}{H}}{\overset{\overset{\displaystyle CH_3}{CH_2-CH_3}}{C}}=C \qquad CH_3-(CH_2)_3-CH_3$$

(a)   (b)   (c)

Reaction 3

$$CH_3-\underset{\underset{\displaystyle CH_3}{|}}{CH}-\underset{\underset{\displaystyle O}{\|}}{C}-O-CH_3 \qquad CH_3-\underset{\underset{\displaystyle CH_3}{|}}{CH}-O-\underset{\underset{\displaystyle O}{\|}}{C}-CH_3 \qquad CH_3-CH_2-\underset{\underset{\displaystyle O}{\|}}{C}-CH_2-CH_3$$

(a)   (b)   (c)

Reaction 4

$$\underset{\underset{\displaystyle CH_2-CH_2}{}}{\overset{\overset{\displaystyle CH_2}{}}{CH_2}}CH-CH=O \qquad \underset{\underset{\displaystyle CH_2-CH-CH_3}{}}{\overset{\overset{\displaystyle CH_2}{}}{CH_2}}C=O \qquad \underset{\underset{\displaystyle CH_2-CH_2}{}}{\overset{\overset{\displaystyle CH_2}{}}{CH_2}}\underset{\underset{\displaystyle O}{\|}}{CH-C}-OH$$

(a)   (b)   (c)

7 UP THE SCALE—GIANT MOLECULES

In your study of the chemistry of carbon compounds you have been concerned with two main themes: (1) the variety of molecular structures possible and the relationship between these and the properties of carbon compounds; and (2) the use of the concept of a functional group to understand their reactions. In this, the final major Section of these Units, we are going to bring these together to study the structure, properties and methods of formation of both natural and manufactured giant molecules. The latter are the building blocks of the thermoplastic materials that now pervade our lives; the former are the basis of much of the chemistry of life itself.

MACROMOLECULE

MONOMER

POLYMER

POLYMERIZATION

ADDITION POLYMER

CONDENSATION POLYMER

HOMOPOLYMER

HETEROPOLYMER

COPOLYMER

BIOPOLYMER

INITIATOR

RADICAL

7.1 THE STRUCTURES OF GIANT MOLECULES

The great variety found in the properties of carbon compounds reflects a similar variety in their molecular structures. This comes not from the presence of a large number of different elements, but from carbon's ability to catenate, to form chains of atoms, apparently without limit. The exploitation of this variety on a massive scale over the past 50 years has had profound effects on society. Some developments, such as the discovery of safe anaesthetics and antibiotics, have been almost wholly beneficial; others, such as the use of halocarbons in aerosol cans and the extensive use of DDT, have given rise to major environmental hazards.

Yet perhaps the most readily apparent and pervasive change has been the substitution of plastics for traditional materials such as glass, wood, paper, cardboard and even metal, and the replacement of natural fibres such as cotton and wool by artificial fibres ('synthetics') such as nylon, polyester and acrylic.

☐ From your own experience, can you suggest some of the reasons for this transformation?

■ In most cases, the change has been for reasons of cost, ease of production, or because the synthetic materials have more desirable properties.

So far you have come across molecules made up of at most a few tens of atoms. Plastics are made up of **macromolecules**, that is, giant molecules often containing thousands of atoms. You might imagine that molecules containing far fewer atoms are complicated enough: how can such giant molecules be manufactured on a large scale?

The process involves the linking together of much smaller molecules, frequently of just one kind, like links in a chain. The small molecules are termed **monomer** molecules, the resultant giant molecule is termed a **polymer**, and the process by which the monomer molecules are linked is called **polymerization**. Polymers can be classified in two ways; according to the way in which the monomers link together, and according to whether the links in the chain, the monomer molecules, are all the same or whether two or more kinds are involved.

There are two main types of reaction involved in producing the polymers we shall be concerned with—addition reactions and condensation reactions—so the polymers are called **addition polymers** and **condensation polymers**, respectively.

If the polymers involve only one kind of monomer molecule they are called **homopolymers**; if two or more are involved then they are called **heteropolymers**. If just two or three types of monomer are involved then they are often called **copolymers** (Figure 28). Each of these terms will become more familiar as you study the rest of the Section. You will find that the synthetic polymers we shall be concerned with include both addition and condensation homopolymers; in contrast, the biological polymers (**biopolymers**) we shall examine are mainly condensation heteropolymers. Let us begin by considering the process of addition polymerization.

(a) A A A A A A A A A

(b) A B C D A B C D A

(c) C A E A A B E D C

(d) A B A B A B A B A

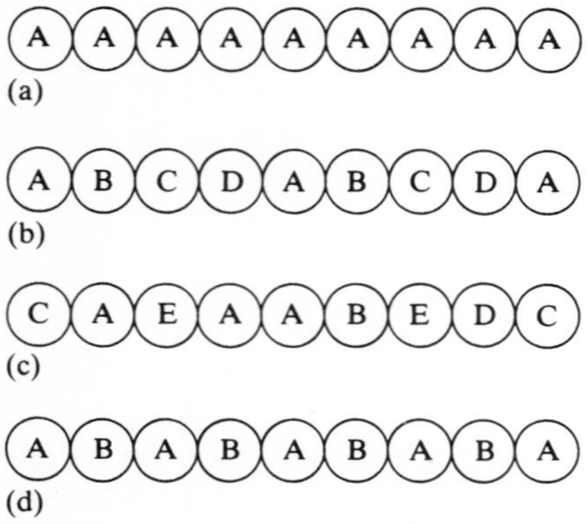

FIGURE 28 Schematic representations of (a) a homopolymer, (b) and (c) heteropolymers and (d) a copolymer. The letters A, B, C etc. are used to indicate different types of monomer.

7.2 ADDITION POLYMERIZATION

You may recall from Section 4.1 that compounds with double bonds, such as ethylene, are said to be unsaturated because the double bond can take part in addition reactions to form two new single bonds; for example:

$$CH_2{=}CH_2 + H_2 \xrightarrow{\text{catalyst}} CH_3{-}CH_3$$

In 1933, R. O. Gibson and E. W. Fawcett at ICI were investigating the reactions of ethylene with other carbon compounds under high pressure. Some of the experiments produced a hard waxy solid which, when analysed, appeared to contain only carbon and hydrogen atoms, in the ratio of $1:2$.

Can you suggest what had happened?

Instead of adding to a *different* type of molecule, the ethylene molecules had added to *one another*, a reaction brought about by the severe conditions used.

$$\cdots + CH_2{=}CH_2 + CH_2{=}CH_2 + CH_2{=}CH_2 + CH_2{=}CH_2 + \cdots$$

$$\downarrow$$

$$\cdots{-}CH_2{-}CH_2{-}CH_2{-}CH_2{-}CH_2{-}CH_2{-}CH_2{-}CH_2{-}\cdots$$

The new substance was a polymer of ethylene, more familiar today as *polythene*. You will see a reconstruction of this experiment in the TV programme 'Man-made macromolecules', using apparatus very similar to that used originally.

This then is one way in which a giant molecule can be formed from smaller ones. The main requirement is the presence in the monomer of a carbon–carbon double bond. Because they are formed by the addition of one monomer molecule to another, they are addition polymers:

> "Can you do addition?", the White Queen asked. "What's one and one and one and one and one and one and one and one and one and one?"
> Lewis Carroll, *Through the Looking-glass*, Macmillan (1872).

A large number of synthetic materials are based on polymers of this type. Many are derived from monomers of the type $CH_2{=}CH{-}X$, where X can be one of a range of atoms or groups. One important monomer not of this type is tetrafluoroethylene, $CF_2{=}CF_2$, which gives the polymer, known variously as PTFE or Teflon, that is used to coat 'non-stick' cooking pans, etc. Some common monomers are listed in Table 13.

TABLE 13   Some common monomers used to form addition polymers

Monomer name*	Abbreviated structural formula of monomer	Polymer name
vinyl chloride (chloroethene)	$CH_2{=}CH{-}Cl$	poly(vinyl chloride), PVC
propylene (propene)	$CH_2{=}CH{-}CH_3$	polypropylene
styrene (phenylethene)	$CH_2{=}CH{-}Ph{\dagger}$	polystyrene

* The common name is given first, followed by the systematic name in brackets.
† Ph is the phenyl group (see Section 4.1).

The formation of addition polymers requires the presence of a small amount of a very reactive substance called an **initiator**. In Gibson and Fawcett's experiments a small amount of oxygen that leaked in acted as the initiator. Usually, though, a substance is used which readily forms molecular fragments that have unpaired electrons. Compounds containing weak covalent bonds, such as peroxides, which have a single bond between two oxygen atoms, break up in this way. When heat or light energy is supplied to such compounds, the O—O bond breaks to give two reactive fragments, each containing one unpaired electron. These fragments are called **radicals**. (Remember that in a structural formula a line denotes a *pair* of bonding electrons; in the following equations, radicals are indicated by the dots on atoms that have an *unpaired* electron.) For example, the initiator di-*tertiary*-butyl peroxide gives rise to methyl radicals, $CH_3 \cdot$, in the following way:

$$CH_3-\underset{\underset{CH_3}{|}}{\overset{\overset{CH_3}{|}}{C}}-O-O-\underset{\underset{CH_3}{|}}{\overset{\overset{CH_3}{|}}{C}}-CH_3 \xrightarrow[\text{ultraviolet radiation}]{\text{heat or}} 2\ CH_3-\underset{\underset{CH_3}{|}}{\overset{\overset{CH_3}{|}}{C}}-O\cdot$$

$$CH_3-\underset{\underset{CH_3}{|}}{\overset{\overset{CH_3}{|}}{C}}-O\cdot \longrightarrow CH_3\cdot + \underset{\underset{CH_3}{|}}{\overset{\overset{CH_3}{|}}{C}}{=}O$$

Once formed, the radicals, $R\cdot$, can react with a molecule of monomer to form a new radical (this too is a radical since it is short of an electron; an odd number plus an even number always gives an odd number). This new radical can react with a further molecule of monomer, and so on. The process is termed chain polymerization; the first three steps are indicated below:

$$R\cdot + CH_2{=}CHX \longrightarrow R-CH_2-\dot{C}HX$$

$$R-CH_2-\dot{C}HX + CH_2{=}CHX \longrightarrow R-CH_2-CHX-CH_2-\dot{C}HX$$

$$R-CH_2-CHX-CH_2-\dot{C}HX + CH_2{=}CHX \longrightarrow R-(CH_2-CHX)_2-CH_2-\dot{C}HX$$

These radicals are so reactive that the whole process of building up a chain of a few hundred monomer units takes but a few seconds. However, because the initial formation of the radicals is a slow process, the complete polymerization can take several hours. So at any instant, the reacting mixture contains initiator, monomer and long-chain polymer, but very few growing chains.

Assuming there are still monomer molecules available, can you suggest what might occur to stop the chain from growing indefinitely?

There is a small, but finite, chance that two growing chains will meet and pair up to form a stable compound:

$$\cdots-CH_2-\dot{C}HX + \dot{C}HX-CH_2-\cdots \longrightarrow \cdots-CH_2-CHX-CHX-CH_2-\cdots$$

If the radical is reactive enough (as it is in the polymerization of ethylene), it can even attach itself to an existing chain. This has an important effect on the properties of the resultant polymer (see Section 7.4).

In the early 1950s, Karl Ziegler in Germany and Giulio Natta in Italy developed a process for the polymerization of compounds containing carbon–carbon double bonds, under very mild conditions. The method involves the use of certain metallic compounds as catalysts and its precise mechanism is too complex to discuss here. However, its discovery transformed the polymer industry, for reasons that will become apparent in Section 7.4. For their work, Ziegler and Natta were jointly awarded the 1963 Nobel Prize for Chemistry.

SAQ 25 Write down the formula of the monomer that would form the following polymer:

$$\cdots-\underset{\underset{O-CH_3}{|}}{\overset{\overset{CH_3}{|}}{\underset{\underset{|}{C{=}O}}{C}}}-CH_2-\underset{\underset{O-CH_3}{|}}{\overset{\overset{CH_3}{|}}{\underset{\underset{|}{C{=}O}}{C}}}-CH_2-\underset{\underset{O-CH_3}{|}}{\overset{\overset{CH_3}{|}}{\underset{\underset{|}{C{=}O}}{C}}}-CH_2-\underset{\underset{O-CH_3}{|}}{\overset{\overset{CH_3}{|}}{\underset{\underset{|}{C{=}O}}{C}}}-CH_2-\underset{\underset{O-CH_3}{|}}{\overset{\overset{CH_3}{|}}{\underset{\underset{|}{C{=}O}}{C}}}-CH_2-\cdots$$

SAQ 26 Outline the first three stages involved in polymerizing monomer A using initiator B. On dissociation, B gives rise to two phenyl radicals, Ph·, and two molecules of carbon dioxide, CO_2.

A $CH_2{=}CH{-}Cl$

B $Ph{-}\underset{\underset{O}{\|}}{C}{-}O{-}O{-}\underset{\underset{O}{\|}}{C}{-}Ph$

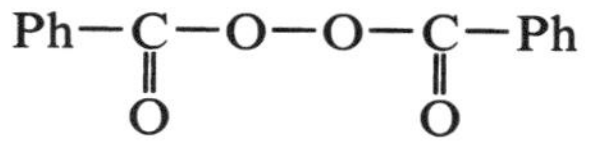

7.3 CONDENSATION POLYMERIZATION

In addition polymerization, the links in the polymer chain are formed sequentially by adding an extra monomer molecule to the growing chain. By contrast, synthetic condensation polymers are formed in a rather different way. The links are frequently formed by the reaction of a carboxylic acid with either an amine or an alcohol. You will recall that acetic acid can react with methanol to form an ester, methyl acetate:

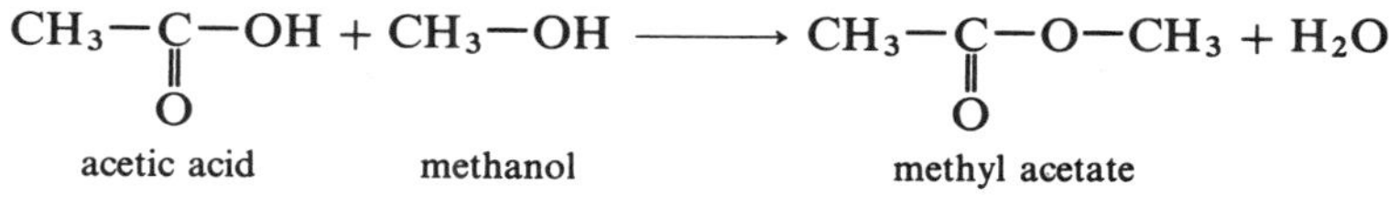

$$CH_3{-}\underset{\underset{O}{\|}}{C}{-}OH + CH_3{-}OH \longrightarrow CH_3{-}\underset{\underset{O}{\|}}{C}{-}O{-}CH_3 + H_2O$$

$$\quad\text{acetic acid}\qquad\qquad\text{methanol}\qquad\qquad\qquad\text{methyl acetate}$$

Similarly, a carboxylic acid can be made to react with an amine, such as methylamine, to give an amide; for example, acetic acid and methylamine react to form N-methylacetamide (the wavy arrow in this and following reactions indicates that more than one step is involved (see Section 6.3)):

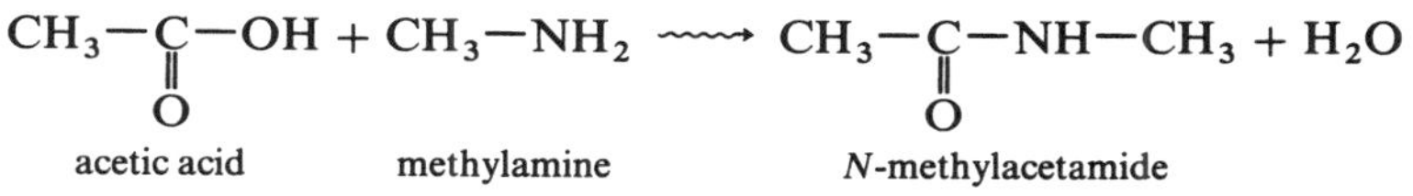

$$CH_3{-}\underset{\underset{O}{\|}}{C}{-}OH + CH_3{-}NH_2 \rightsquigarrow CH_3{-}\underset{\underset{O}{\|}}{C}{-}NH{-}CH_3 + H_2O$$

$$\quad\text{acetic acid}\qquad\qquad\text{methylamine}\qquad\qquad\text{N-methylacetamide}$$

Note that in both cases a molecule of water is formed. As you know from Section 6.3, such reactions, in which two molecules link up with the expulsion of a smaller molecule, are known as condensation reactions.

> See if you can write down the products that would be formed (a) from the condensation of acetic acid with hexane-1,6-diamine, $NH_2{-}(CH_2)_6{-}NH_2$; and (b) from the condensation of methylamine with hexanedioic acid,
>
> $$HO{-}\underset{\underset{O}{\|}}{C}{-}(CH_2)_4{-}\underset{\underset{O}{\|}}{C}{-}OH.$$

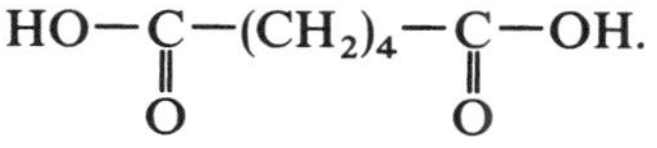

In each case two amide links could be formed as shown:

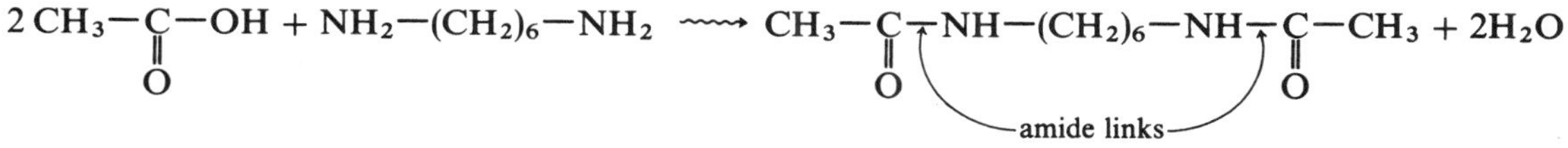

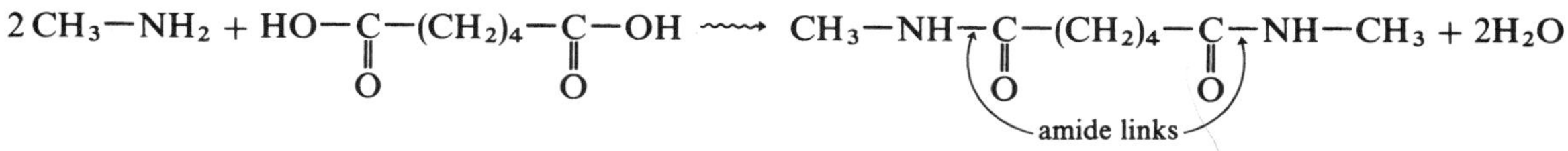

$$2\,CH_3{-}\underset{\underset{O}{\|}}{C}{-}OH + NH_2{-}(CH_2)_6{-}NH_2 \rightsquigarrow CH_3{-}\underset{\underset{O}{\|}}{C}{-}NH{-}(CH_2)_6{-}NH{-}\underset{\underset{O}{\|}}{C}{-}CH_3 + 2H_2O$$

$$\text{amide links}$$

$$2\,CH_3{-}NH_2 + HO{-}\underset{\underset{O}{\|}}{C}{-}(CH_2)_4{-}\underset{\underset{O}{\|}}{C}{-}OH \rightsquigarrow CH_3{-}NH{-}\underset{\underset{O}{\|}}{C}{-}(CH_2)_4{-}\underset{\underset{O}{\|}}{C}{-}NH{-}CH_3 + 2H_2O$$

$$\text{amide links}$$

So the presence of two functional groups in just *one* of the reactants is insufficient to form a polymer.

> Suppose instead the diamine was reacted with the dicarboxylic acid. Would you expect a polymer to be formed?

If your answer is yes, you arrived at the same conclusion as Wallace Carothers reached in 1935 when he was working at the du Pont company in the USA. Carothers carried out this reaction and so formed the first artificial

POLYAMIDE

POLYESTER

polyamide, a substance more familiar as *nylon*. He chose these particular compounds rather than other members of the homologous series because they were easier, and cheaper, to obtain.

$$n \, HO-\underset{\underset{O}{\|}}{C}-(CH_2)_4-\underset{\underset{O}{\|}}{C}-OH + n \, NH_2-(CH_2)_6-NH_2 \longrightarrow$$

$$H-\left[-NH-(CH_2)_6-NH-\underset{\underset{O}{\|}}{C}-(CH_2)_4-\underset{\underset{O}{\|}}{C}-\right]_n-OH + (2n-1) \, H_2O$$

nylon

Because each amide link is formed in an individual reaction, the polymer is formed stepwise and the process is termed step polymerization: the monomer soon forms short chains and these growing chains link together, and so on. Because of this, if the polymerization were stopped part-way, the sample would consist of intermediate-sized chains with very little monomer and very few long polymer molecules.

The polymer formed from hexane-1,6-diamine and hexanedioic acid is called nylon-6,6 because each of the reactants contains six carbon atoms. In principle, a great variety of such polymers could be made with different numbers of carbon atoms in each of the two monomers. In practice, because of the availability and cost of the reactants, the only other commercially important nylon of this type is nylon-6,10, in which the same diamine is used but the dicarboxylic acid has ten carbon atoms. However, by comparison with nylon-6,6, nylon-6,10 is produced on a small scale.

The formation of a polyamide required the reaction of molecules with two functional groups. Can you suggest how a polyamide could be formed by using a *single* monomer?

$$NH_2-(CH_2)_5-\underset{\underset{O}{\|}}{C}-OH$$

6-aminohexanoic acid

To form an amide, an amino group and a carboxyl group are required. If these were present in the same molecule, it would form a polyamide. In fact the other major type of nylon is nylon-6, in which the monomer is 6-aminohexanoic acid.

$$n \, NH_2-(CH_2)_5-\underset{\underset{O}{\|}}{C}-OH \longrightarrow H-\left[-NH-(CH_2)_5-\underset{\underset{O}{\|}}{C}-\right]_n-OH + (n-1) \, H_2O$$

nylon-6

The reaction of a carboxylic acid with an alcohol to form an ester is also a condensation reaction that can form the basis of a polymer. You almost certainly know the name for such a polymer, even though you may not realize it; it is, by analogy with polyamide, **polyester**. The commercially most important polyester derives from the monomers 1,4-benzenedicarboxylic acid and ethane-1,2-diol:*

$$n \, HO-CH_2-CH_2-OH + n \, HO-\underset{\underset{O}{\|}}{C}-\!\!\left\langle\!\!\!\bigcirc\!\!\!\right\rangle\!\!-\underset{\underset{O}{\|}}{C}-OH \longrightarrow$$

ethane-1,2-diol   1,4-benzenedicarboxylic acid

$$H-\left[-O-CH_2-CH_2-O-\underset{\underset{O}{\|}}{C}-\!\!\left\langle\!\!\!\bigcirc\!\!\!\right\rangle\!\!-\underset{\underset{O}{\|}}{C}-\right]_n-OH + 2n \, H_2O$$

polyester

This polyester is known as Terylene in the United Kingdom and Dacron in the USA.

---

* Compounds containing two —OH groups are known collectively as diols.

SAQ 27 You are given three pairs of statements (a)–(c) below. The statements are in the following form:

Statement 1

BECAUSE

Statement 2

You are asked to decide first whether each statement of the pair is true or false. Then if both statements are true, you are asked to decide whether statement 2 is a correct explanation of statement 1. For each question, choose *one* answer from the key.

KEY

A Both statements are false

B Statement 1 is false but statement 2 is true

C Statement 1 is true but statement 2 is false

D Both statements are true, but statement 2 is *not* a correct explanation of statement 1

E Both statements are true, and statement 2 *is* a correct explanation of statement 1

(a) *Statement 1* The formation of PVC from vinyl chloride is an addition polymerization

BECAUSE

Statement 2 The reaction can be carried out with a radical initiator.

(b) *Statement 1* Condensation polymerization involves the expulsion of a small molecule such as water at each step, whereas this does not occur in addition polymerization

BECAUSE

Statement 2 Condensation polymers always require two reactants as starting materials, whereas addition polymers are normally prepared from one monomer.

(c) *Statement 1* X will form a condensation polymer with Y but not with Z

BECAUSE

Statement 2 Z has only one carboxyl group.

$$NH_2-(CH_2)_3-NH_2 \quad HO-\underset{\underset{O}{\|}}{C}-(CH_2)_3-\underset{\underset{O}{\|}}{C}-OH \quad NH_2-(CH_2)_3-\underset{\underset{O}{\|}}{C}-OH$$

$$X \qquad\qquad\qquad Y \qquad\qquad\qquad Z$$

SAQ 28 Classify the molecular structures A–F as one of the following: initiator, condensation polymer, addition polymer, monomer for condensation polymerization, monomer for addition polymerization.

A $\cdots-\underset{Ph}{CH}-CH_2-\underset{Ph}{CH}-CH_2-\underset{Ph}{CH}-CH_2-\underset{Ph}{CH}-CH_2-\underset{Ph}{CH}-CH_2-\underset{Ph}{CH}-\cdots$

B $\cdots-NH-\underset{\underset{O}{\|}}{C}-(CH_2)_5-NH-\underset{\underset{O}{\|}}{C}-(CH_2)_5-NH-\underset{\underset{O}{\|}}{C}-(CH_2)_5-NH-\underset{\underset{O}{\|}}{C}-\cdots$

C $CH_3-(CH_2)_{10}-\underset{\underset{O}{\|}}{C}-O-O-\underset{\underset{O}{\|}}{C}-(CH_2)_{10}-CH_3$

D $HO-\underset{\underset{O}{\|}}{C}-(CH_2)_8-\underset{\underset{O}{\|}}{C}-OH$

E $CH_2{=}CCl_2$

F $\cdots-CF_2-CF_2-CF_2-CF_2-CF_2-CF_2-CF_2-CF_2-CF_2-\cdots$

CRYSTALLITE

PLASTICIZER

7.4 THE PROPERTIES OF GIANT MOLECULES

Since the Second World War, giant molecules have become the object of one of the most intense investigations in the history of science. The development of synthetic materials based on polymers has reached the stage where a polymer chemist can, in a sense, design a particular polymer to order. What, then, are the chief determining factors in the relationship between molecular structure and macroscopic properties?

> Apart from their size, polymers are different from other compounds you have come across in these Units so far. Can you spot the difference?

Generally, chemists are much concerned with chemical purity, and take great care to study samples containing just one type of molecule. Consequently, we normally expect that the properties of a particular sample would be the same as for any other sample. But the properties of a polymer depend critically on the conditions employed in its formation. Further, because individual molecules may have grown to different extents before the process stopped, it is not possible to specify a single molecular mass. The best that can be achieved is to aim for a polymer that has a narrow range of molecular masses.

Another way in which polymers differ from much smaller molecules is the way in which they pack together. Smaller molecules generally form crystals in which the molecules are packed in a regular array, for example the I_2 molecule (Units 13–14). On heating, the solid crystal eventually melts at a precise melting temperature (provided it does not first decompose). By contrast, many synthetic polymers do not readily form crystals. Instead the molecules are twisted and coiled rather like cooked spaghetti (Figure 29). At low temperatures, little movement of the molecules is possible, and the material is hard and brittle. As the temperature is increased, the chains become more mobile. There is no particular temperature at which the polymer can be said to have melted, only a range of temperatures over which it gradually softens*. This allows the material to be moulded or extruded† in the fabrication process, but sets an upper limit to the temperature at which the article can be used.

Although polymers do not pack in a regular array, a technique known as X-ray crystallography shows that segments of the polymer chain are lined up with one another as shown in Figure 30. These aligned segments form regions called **crystallites**; some polymers contain more than others. They

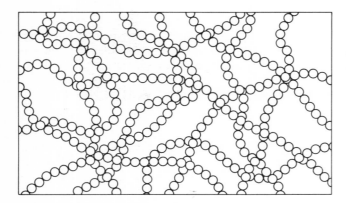

FIGURE 29   Schematic representation of the random arrangement of the molecules in many polymers. Each circle represents a monomer unit.

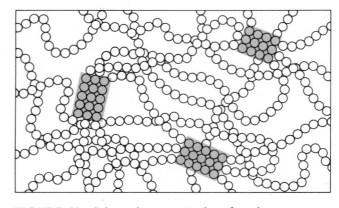

FIGURE 30   Schematic representation of a polymer containing crystallites. The crystallites are the areas shown in pink.

* This is true of the so-called *thermoplastic* polymers, but not of the *thermosetting* variety such as Bakelite. However, we are only concerned here with thermoplastics.

† Extrusion is the operation whereby rods, tubes and various solid and hollow sections are produced by forcing the polymer through an appropriately shaped die by means of a ram.

(a)

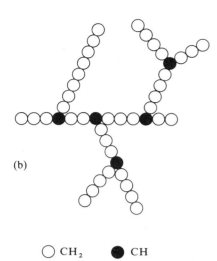

(b)

○ CH₂　● CH

FIGURE 31　Chain structure of polythene: (a) high-density polymer; (b) low-density polymer.

are found to occur in greatest number when there are relatively few branches in the chain. The presence of a large number of crystallites confers rigidity, coupled with strength, to an extent far greater than that obtained in substances consisting mostly of haphazard entangled chains.

□ Why do you think this is so?

■ The magnitudes of the forces between molecules increase as the separation between them decreases. The crystallites are regions where adjacent molecules are closest together, and hence the intermolecular forces are greatest within the crystallites. So the more crystallites there are, the stronger is the material.

Polythene formed by the high-pressure method described in Section 7.2 does not give the idealized straight-chain polymer shown in Figure 31a. Because the growing radicals are so reactive, they can attack existing polymer chains so producing long branches (Figure 31b). The molecules cannot pack closely, rendering this *high-pressure* polymer (also referred to as *low-density* polythene) flexible, but decreasing the possibility of forming crystallites. By contrast, the polymerization process developed by Ziegler and Natta (Section 7.2) does not involve radicals, and leads to linear polymeric molecules (Figure 31a). This *low-pressure* polymer (also called *high-density* polythene) is much more crystalline and rigid, and has a higher softening temperature then the other form.

Figure 32 shows two otherwise identical plastic bottles, one made from high-density polythene, which is rigid, and the other made of low-density polythene. Both forms are widely used. Low-density polythene is less expensive and so is the form used for sheeting, containers and other household goods. High-density polythene is used for, among other things, medical equipment: high-density polythene can be sterilized with steam, whereas, because of its lower softening temperature, the low-density form would be deformed. Polypropylene (formed using Ziegler–Natta catalysts) is even better than high-density polythene in this respect.

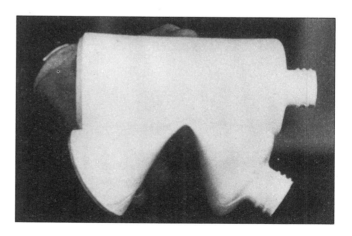

FIGURE 32　Two bottles made from polythene. The upper one is made from high-density polythene, the lower one from low-density polythene.

Although variation in molecular structure forms the basis of much of the diversity in properties among plastics, some synthetic materials owe their characteristics to the use of additives. Poly(vinyl chloride) (PVC), for example, is a rigid material at ordinary temperatures and is much used for the manufacture of pipes, mouldings and panels. The addition of small quantities of low-molecular-mass esters, however, produces a much more pliable material. The incorporation of such additives, known as **plasticizers**, makes PVC sufficiently flexible to be used as the insulating material for electric cable, simulated leather, flexible sheeting and 'cling film' for the packaging of foods. Concern about the possible toxic effects of the plasticizers when in direct contact with food has led to the increasing use of other polymers such as low-density polythene for this latter purpose.

The use of polymers is not confined to applications in which they replace traditional materials such as wood or paper; polymers may also be used to replace or supplement natural fibres such as cotton and silk (Plates 9a and 9b, and Figure 33). Giant molecules should form strong fibres, provided they can be aligned like a bundle of straight twigs; alignment is facilitated by the absence of branches. That is one of the reasons why condensation polymers are such good fibre-forming polymers: their method of formation is such that there can be no branches. Another reason is that the cohesive forces between the chains are strong.

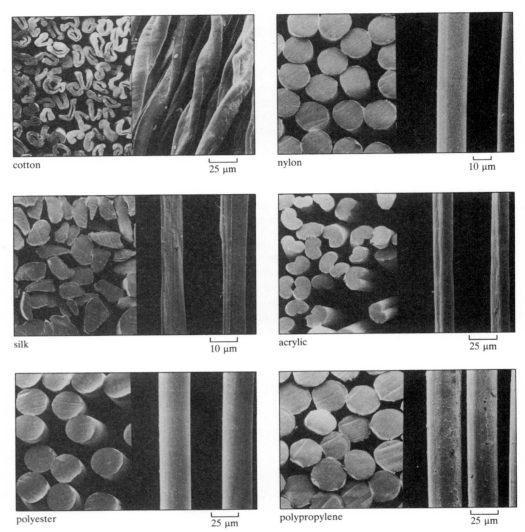

cotton   25 μm

nylon   10 μm

silk   10 μm

acrylic   25 μm

polyester   25 μm

polypropylene   25 μm

FIGURE 33 Cross-section and lengthways photographs produced by scanning electron microscopy of selected widely-used natural and synthetic fibres.

FIGURE 34 Structure of parts of two adjacent nylon molecules.

As you know, nylon is a very good fibre-forming polymer. Look at Figure 34, which shows the structure of parts of two adjacent nylon chains. See if you can deduce the nature of the cohesive forces between them.

You will recall (Section 2.2) that hydroxyl (—OH) groups and amino (—NH₂) groups can form hydrogen bonds. Now a hydrogen bond requires only that a hydrogen atom be attached to one of the two atoms of high electronegativity involved. So the N—H groups in one nylon chain can form hydrogen bonds with the oxygen atom of the C=O groups in a neighbouring chain. You can indicate this on the diagram by drawing a dashed line between each of the three N—H/C=O pairs that face one another. In the same way, hydrogen bonding can be extended to other adjacent chains.

So in a sample of nylon we can expect to find whole sections of molecules lined up (Figure 35a). Furthermore, by mechanically stretching the nylon as it cools, these lined-up sections can be made parallel to one another (Figure 35b). The result, on the macroscopic scale, is a very strong fibre.

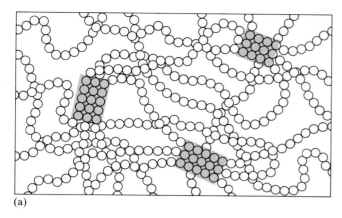

FIGURE 35 Schematic representation of (a) unorientated and (b) orientated nylon molecules.

Hydrogen bonding, the main contributor to the cohesive forces between nylon chains, is one of the three types of force mentioned in Section 2.2 that exist between covalent molecules.

> Can you recall the other two types of force between covalent molecules?

There are the dipole–dipole attractions that exist between polar parts of the molecules and the London forces that exist between all molecules. The latter become more important as the relative molecular mass increases.

> Terylene (polyester) and polypropylene (Figure 36) also form fibres: they are both used to manufacture textiles (Plates 9a and 9b), the latter additionally for string and rope. Which of the three types of cohesive force are involved in each case?

(a)

$$\cdots -O-CH_2-CH_2-O-\underset{O}{\overset{\|}{C}}-\bigcirc-\underset{O}{\overset{\|}{C}}-O-CH_2-CH_2-O-\underset{O}{\overset{\|}{C}}-\bigcirc-\underset{O}{\overset{\|}{C}}-\cdots$$

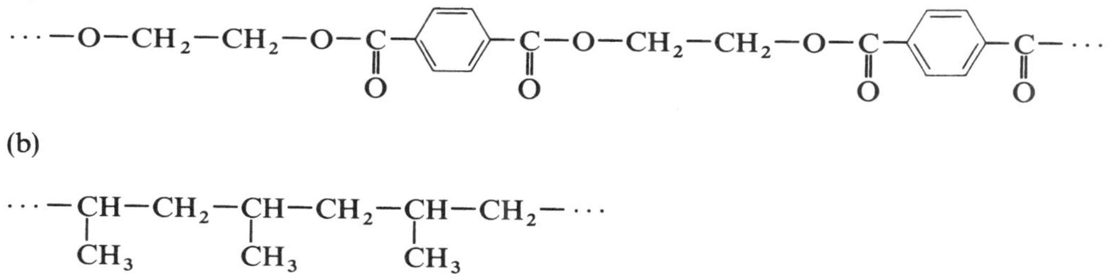

FIGURE 36 Structure of (a) part of a polyester molecule and (b) part of a polypropylene molecule.

(b)

$$\cdots -\underset{CH_3}{\overset{|}{C}H}-CH_2-\underset{CH_3}{\overset{|}{C}H}-CH_2-\underset{CH_3}{\overset{|}{C}H}-CH_2-\cdots$$

There are no O—H or N—H groups in either polymer, so hydrogen bonding is not involved. The C=O and C—O groups in Terylene are polar, so both the remaining types of force are involved in this polymer. In polypropylene, there are no polar groups, so only London forces are involved. It is its highly regular structure that enables fibres to form.

Although originally used mainly as a fibre for the manufacture of a variety of textiles, polyester is now increasingly finding a use as a bulk plastic for the manufacture of soft drink bottles. If you look carefully when you visit your local supermarket, you may well see the boxes containing such bottles marked PET, which stands for polyethylene terephthalate (from the older name, terephthalic acid, instead of 1,4-benzenedicarboxylic acid). In 1985, 475 000 tonnes were used world-wide for this purpose. Other uses of this versatile polymer include photographic film, recording tape, computer 'floppy' disks, electrical insulation and tyre reinforcement.

SAQ 29 The polymer known as Orlon has the structure given below. It has good fibre-forming properties. X-ray crystallography indicates relatively few crystallites.

(a) What is the monomer corresponding to this polymer?
(b) Outline briefly the reasons why it is used as a fibre.

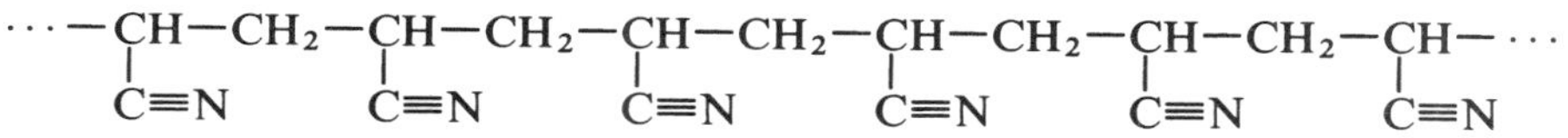

$$\cdots -\underset{C\equiv N}{\overset{|}{C}H}-CH_2-\underset{C\equiv N}{\overset{|}{C}H}-CH_2-\underset{C\equiv N}{\overset{|}{C}H}-CH_2-\underset{C\equiv N}{\overset{|}{C}H}-CH_2-\underset{C\equiv N}{\overset{|}{C}H}-CH_2-\underset{C\equiv N}{\overset{|}{C}H}-\cdots$$

structure of Orlon

"AH, HA!"

$$NH_2-CH-C-OH$$

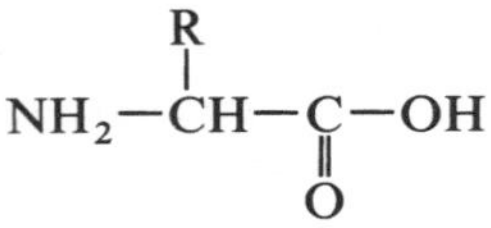

general formula
of amino acids

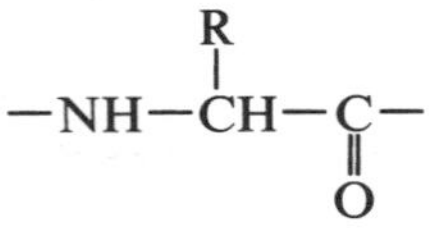

$$-NH-CH-C-$$

an amino acid residue

7.5 BIOLOGICAL MACROMOLECULES

You may recall from Section 5.2 that the 20 or so naturally occurring amino acids (with the general formula shown) are the building blocks of **proteins**. By analogy with nylon-6 (Section 7.2), it is not unreasonable to suggest that proteins too are polyamides. This is indeed the case; proteins have the structures shown below. Each segment derived from an individual amino acid monomer is called an **amino acid residue**.

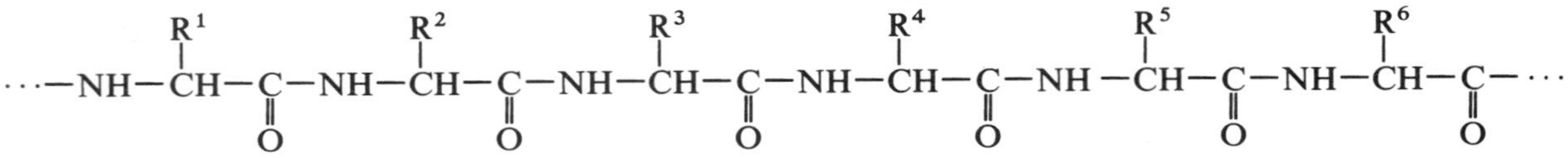

$$\cdots-NH-CH-C-NH-CH-C-NH-CH-C-NH-CH-C-NH-CH-C-NH-CH-C-\cdots$$

section of a protein molecule

Note however that proteins consist not of a single type of amino acid residue, as in nylon-6, but of a selection of the 20 possibilities that occur in nature. As a consequence, the groups R^1, R^2, R^3 etc. vary according to the protein and may be the same as each other or different. In other words, whereas, for example, nylon-6 is a homopolymer, proteins are examples of heteropolymers.

Proteins are also known as **polypeptides** though this term is used most frequently for short chains containing relatively few amino acid residues. If polypeptides are boiled with dilute acid or dilute alkali, they are broken down into their constituent amino acids, a process called hydrolysis (Section 6.3). Powerful enzymes in your stomach and small intestine also catalyse the hydrolysis of proteins to amino acids, a prerequisite, as you will see in Unit 22, for the synthesis of the proteins your body requires.

You will learn more of the role of proteins in later Units, particularly Unit 22. Suffice it to say at this stage that proteins are of two general types, **fibrous proteins** and **globular proteins**. Fibrous proteins have highly repetitive sequences of amino acids and are of varying lengths, like synthetic polyamides. Globular proteins, on the other hand, are of fixed length. Further, the amino acid sequences found in globular proteins are highly varied, though the sequence in any particular one is very specific and is the key to its biochemical function. While the polymerization of a single amino acid in the laboratory may be a relatively straightforward matter, the synthesis of a particular globular protein is a challenge of quite a different order! You can imagine how many different chains can be made given a choice of 20 possibilities for each additional amino acid residue attached. Clearly, the vast array of different proteins found in living systems demonstrates very well the importance of this particular type of condensation polymer in the chemistry of life.

So, too, do two other classes of biological condensation polymer—the **polysaccharides** and **polynucleotides**. We shall say little about the first of these—you will learn more about them in Unit 22—except to note that many well known polysaccharides (for example, starch) are homopolymers in which the constituent monomer is the simple sugar glucose. However, as polynucleotides figure rather importantly in the next Unit (the first of those devoted to biology), it is worthwhile giving them a brief introduction here.

Just as protein and polypeptide are alternative names for the same thing, so also is there another name for the polynucleotides, that is the **nucleic acids**. The two main categories of nucleic acid found in nature are **DNA** (**de**oxyribonucleic acid) and **RNA** (ribonucleic acid) and, one way or another, both these substances are crucially involved in the way genetic information is stored and used. As you progress through the biology Units, the fascinating story of the chemical nature and biological functioning of these molecules will become very familiar to you. For now, we shall introduce you to the chemistry of DNA (we will leave RNA until Unit 24).

As the name polynucleotide suggests, molecules in this group are polymers (in fact, condensation polymers) in which the constituent monomers are **nucleotides**. DNA is a heteropolymer. There are four different monomers, these being four different *deoxyribo*nucleotides which we represent for now by the letters pdA, pdG, pdC and pdT (you will see why in a moment). Just as with a globular protein, the sequence of nucleotide residues found is highly varied; a typical segment might be as follows:

$$\cdots-pdG-pdG-pdA-pdT-pdC-pdC-pdT-pdA-pdT-pdG-\cdots$$

But what do these letters represent? What are the structures of these four monomers with such a long collective name, deoxyribonucleotide? Each one is made up of a phosphate group joined to a molecule of deoxyribose* joined to one of four different kinds of base, adenine, guanine, cytosine and thymine.

adenine (A) guanine (G) cytosine (C) thymine (T)

So, representing phosphate by 'p', deoxyribose by 'd', and the four bases by 'A', 'G', 'C' and 'T', we have the following.

$$pdA = phosphate - deoxyribose - adenine$$
$$pdG = phosphate - deoxyribose - guanine$$
$$pdC = phosphate - deoxyribose - cytosine$$
$$pdT = phosphate - deoxyribose - thymine$$

* Deoxyribose is a sugar containing five carbon atoms per molecule. Glucose, a more commonly known sugar, has six carbons per molecule, and sucrose (the substance we all know as 'sugar') has 12 carbon atoms per molecule.

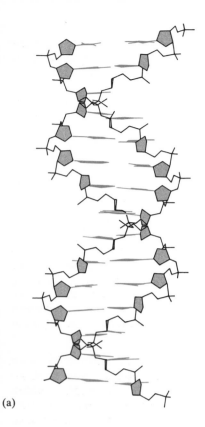

(a)

In fact DNA consists of not just one but *two* strands of polydeoxyribonucleotide wound round each other in a double helix (Figure 37). The two strands are linked by hydrogen bonds between the N—H group on one base and the O and N atoms on another (Figure 38). The nucleotide sequences shown on p. 89 and in Figure 38 are invented. In nature, the actual sequence is of absolutely crucial importance as DNA is the very blueprint of life, a blueprint which, among other things, contains the instructions for the polymerization of amino acids to form proteins, a process in which the precise pattern of hydrogen bonds linking the two polynucleotide strands plays a key role.

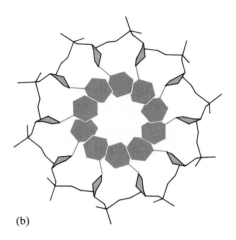

(b)

FIGURE 37 (a) Section of a DNA molecule showing the twisted pair of polynucleotide chains (the 'double helix'); (b) view down the helix axis. The bases are shown in red, the deoxyribose units in grey and the phosphate links in black.

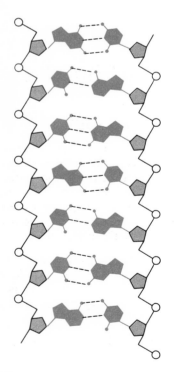

FIGURE 38 Section of a DNA molecule showing the two polynucleotide chains, held together by hydrogen bonding between pairs of bases, one on each strand. As in the previous Figure, the bases are shown in red, the deoxyribose units in grey and the phosphate links in black.

SUMMARY OF SECTION 7

One of the most obvious and pervasive changes since the Second World War has been the substitution of synthetic materials for more traditional natural ones. These materials are generally based on giant molecules, polymers, assembled by linking together hundreds of small molecules, known as monomers. Polymers in which just one kind of monomer is involved are known as homopolymers, and as heteropolymers when more than one kind of monomer is used. Polymers can be classified according to the way in which they are formed. There are two main types, addition polymers and condensation polymers.

Addition polymers have the following characteristics. They are formed from monomers that contain a carbon–carbon double bond. The polymerization process is started by the formation of radicals from an initiator. Once started, the chain grows by addition of a monomer molecule to the growing radicals to form another radical. The process is stopped when two radicals combine. The growth of an individual chain takes just a few seconds, although the bulk polymerization might take some hours. Consequently, part-way through the polymerization process, the reaction mixture contains mainly monomer and high-molecular-mass polymer. Because the intermediates are so reactive, extensive branching can often occur.

By contrast, condensation polymers are formed from molecules with two functional groups. Molecules of monomer link together with the expulsion of a small molecule, such as H_2O. The polymer chains are formed in a stepwise process in which the monomer is consumed early on, but the molecular mass of the whole mixture increases only slowly. Since the intermediates are much less reactive than in addition polymerization, branching does not occur. Condensation polymers are of two main types: polyamides (formed from the reaction of a diamine and a dicarboxylic acid or from an amino acid) and polyesters (formed from a diol and a dicarboxylic acid).

CHEMICAL EVOLUTION

Because of the random way in which the growth of the polymer chains is stopped, a given polymer sample has a range of molecular masses. Because of this, and because the chains are so long, polymers do not readily form crystals. However, small areas of crystallinity, called crystallites, do occur. Polythene formed by high-pressure polymerization (low-density polythene) has many branches and few crystallites. It is therefore flexible and softens at a relatively low temperature. Polythene (and polypropylene) formed by Ziegler–Natta polymerization is linear. It is therefore more rigid and softens at a higher temperature. The addition of plasticizers can convert rigid polymer into a more flexible material.

Polymers with groups that can hydrogen bond or that are polar form fibres. Examples are nylon and Terylene. Polypropylene (formed by the Ziegler–Natta process) can also form fibres because it has a highly regular molecular structure.

Proteins and polypeptides are polyamides formed from the 20 naturally-occurring amino acids, and are therefore heteropolymers. There are two main types of proteins: fibrous proteins have highly repetitive sequences of amino acid residues and are of varying length; globular proteins in contrast, are of fixed length and have a wide variety of amino acid sequences. The sequence in any one protein is, however, very specific and the key to its function.

Two other biologically important macromolecules are also condensation polymers. These are polysaccharides and polynucleotides. The former are polymers of sugars, of which glucose is a well known example. Another name for a polynucleotide is nucleic acid. The two main categories of polynucleotide are DNA (deoxyribonucleic acid) and RNA (ribonucleic acid). The nucleotide corresponding to DNA is made up of a phosphate group, a deoxyribose molecule (another sugar) and one of four organic bases, adenine, guanine, cytosine and thymine. DNA is the blueprint of life itself, in which hydrogen bonding plays a key role in carrying out the instructions incorporated within its structure.

8 INTO THE PAST—PREBIOTIC CHEMISTRY

8.1 PREBIOTIC CARBON COMPOUNDS

Of all the questions posed in humanity's quest for knowledge, perhaps the most fascinating concerns the origin of life itself. The development of Charles Darwin's theory of evolution by natural selection in the middle of the 19th century (Unit 19) opened the door to the realization that such a question could be amenable to scientific investigation. The logical extension of evolutionary theory was the concept of **chemical evolution**, the idea that life evolved on Earth from simpler non-living prebiotic substances.

It was not until the 1920s that Alexander Oparin in Russia and J. B. S. Haldane in Britain independently put forward the ideas that have formed the basis for many of the current theories of the origin of life. They postulated that the primordial atmosphere contained not oxygen, but hydrogen, ammonia, and methane.

> Can you recall from Section 2.3 what would be the effect of the absence of oxygen in the atmosphere?

Without oxygen there would be no protective ozone. Consequently, ultra-violet radiation from the Sun could penetrate the atmosphere and cause photochemical reactions to occur on the surface of the Earth. Other reactions might have been initiated by lightning. These reactions could lead to the formation of larger molecules, which would be washed into the ocean. Over a period of perhaps a thousand million years, these molecules could have reacted further to give rise to the compounds necessary for life.

It was not until 1953 that Stanley Miller, working in Chicago, provided the first experimental test of this hypothesis. The apparatus he used is shown in Figure 39. The lower flask contained water, and the rest of the apparatus was filled with a mixture of hydrogen, ammonia and methane. The gases were made to circulate past the sparking electrodes by boiling the water, which reliquefied in the condenser and washed any soluble products down into the lower flask.

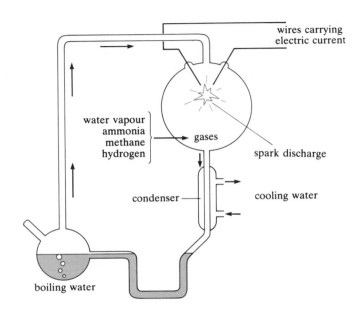

FIGURE 39 Miller's apparatus for the simulation of primitive Earth conditions.

☐ What do you suppose the electric discharge and the water in the lower flask were meant to represent?

■ The electric discharge was supposed to simulate the effect of lightning and the water in the lower flask was meant to represent the ocean.

After a week, the solution was analysed carefully. To his delight, Miller found that several of the natural amino acids had been formed in substantial amounts: glycine, alanine and aspartic acid, for example, were all identified.

When faced with unexpected products from a reaction, chemists endeavour to provide explanations based on known molecular properties. Miller was no exception. It was already known that glycine can be formed from the reaction of ammonia, NH_3, formaldehyde, $CH_2{=}O$, and hydrogen cyanide, $H{-}C{\equiv}N$. Miller was able to demonstrate that formaldehyde and hydrogen cyanide were indeed formed initially in his experiments, and ammonia, of course, was present already.

Since Miller's initial work, there have been numerous similar experiments in which a variety of different gas mixtures have been investigated, using diverse energy sources, with the result that nearly all the naturally occurring amino acids have been made in this way. In the majority of cases, however, the gas mixture has been reducing, not oxidizing as the Earth's atmosphere is today. Few scientists now doubt the Oparin–Haldane hypothesis that our present atmosphere has evolved from one of quite different composition.

8.2 THE ORIGIN OF OPTICAL ACTIVITY

Experiments such as Miller's provide a possible mechanism for the formation of amino acids, the building blocks of proteins. But you will recall that, apart from glycine, all the naturally occurring amino acids are chiral.

Would you expect the amino acids produced in such experiments to be optically active?

Since Miller employed no chiral agent, the amino acids he obtained were racemic mixtures: none of the starting compounds was chiral, so there was an equal probability that both optical isomers would be formed. As Miller's experiments involved of the order of 10^{20} molecules, it is not very surprising to find equal numbers of each optical isomer were produced, *within the accuracy of his measurements*. But it is almost impossible for a sample to be absolutely optically inactive. It is much more probable that a slight excess of one isomer will be present, and the smaller the number of molecules in a sample, the more significant the excess is likely to become.

One characteristic of living systems is the phenomenon of growth. In the prebiotic phase, growth would have involved the formation of large molecules from smaller ones. This could have provided a mechanism for amplifying any slight bias towards one isomer. If so, the occurrence of L-amino acids, as opposed to the D isomers, is purely a matter of chance. Many scientists working in the field, however, are sceptical of this idea of a chiral molecular 'Adam', and prefer to believe in the presence of a chiral agent in the environment. If so, then the occurrence of L-amino acids is not a matter of chance: their formation would have been favoured over the formation of the D isomers.

One intriguing possibility arises from the fact that matter itself appears to be one-handed. It has been shown that particles emitted from certain radioactive isotopes are predominantly of one-handedness*.

Such high-energy particles can cause chemical reactions to occur. The most fascinating aspect of this hypothesis is that it has attracted some experimental support. William Bonner and his co-workers at Stanford University in the USA reported in 1977 that they had irradiated racemic leucine (one of the naturally occurring amino acids) with artificially produced high-energy electrons. Electrons of the natural handedness caused the D-leucine to be degraded preferentially, leaving an excess of the (naturally occurring) L isomer. Electrons of the opposite handedness left an excess of the D isomer. Since then, calculations have shown that this natural chirality of fundamental particles favours the naturally occurring amino acids and sugars, although the difference in energy between the two optical isomers is very small; for example, for alanine, the energy difference is such that, for every mole (6.023×10^{23} molecules) of alanine produced, there would be an excess of only 10^6 molecules of the L isomer over the D isomer.

So far, these, and any other possibilities, are little more than hypotheses. There have been few conclusive results. By the very nature of the problem, it is likely that the best that can be hoped for is a most probable hypothesis based on a mechanism shown to work in a model system. None the less, the origin of one-handedness in the molecules of life, one of the fundamental aspects of the origin of life, remains one of the most fascinating puzzles in science.

8.3 POSTSCRIPT

If the chemical evolution hypothesis is correct, then it is likely that life is not unique to the Earth. So far, there is no evidence of life elsewhere in the Universe. There is, however, evidence of prebiotic molecules relevant to Miller-type experiments.

First, it is possible, using techniques of radio-astronomy, to detect and identify the presence of molecules in interstellar space. Prominent among these are formaldehyde and hydrogen cyanide, the precursors to the amino acids arising from Miller-type experiments.

---

* Matter, in the majority of cases, exhibits no distinction between interactions in a particular system of particles and similar interactions in the mirror-image system. However, it was predicted by Chen Ning Yang and Tsung Dao Lee in 1956 and shown experimentally soon after by Madame Chien-Shung Wu, all Chinese-born physicists working in the USA, that in certain cases there is a distinction. This is related to a fundamental property of elementary particles called *parity*.

Second, careful analysis of a meteorite that fell near the town of Murchison in Australia in 1969 revealed a selection of amino acids similar to those formed in electric-discharge experiments. As with the amino acids synthesized in Miller's experiments, these were also optically inactive. The discovery of extraterrestrial amino acids confirms in a striking way the general ideas about prebiotic carbon chemistry derived from Miller-type experiments.

It has doubtless become apparent to you that studies aimed at elucidating the origin of life draw on techniques and knowledge from physics, biology and Earth sciences as well as chemistry. Such investigations, though having profound philosophical implications, are of little immediate practical importance. However, such a transdisciplinary approach is becoming increasingly necessary for the solution of many of the problems presently facing society.

Humanity's attempts to control the environment have resulted in an increase in the quality of life for many people. Equally, they have created new hazards, such as pollution. In the future, the search will need to be for a more responsive technology, one based on a better understanding of the delicate balance of the chemical, physical and biological processes involved in the biosphere. As far as the chemist is concerned, this will require a deeper understanding of the chemical and physical behaviour of natural and synthetic substances and the way these properties are linked to molecular structure.

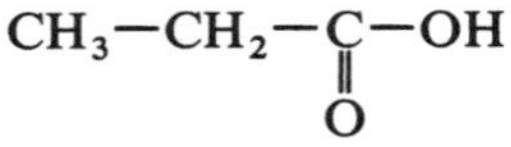

$$CH_3-CH_2-\underset{\underset{O}{\|}}{C}-OH$$

propanoic acid

$$CH_3-\underset{\underset{O}{\|}}{C}-O-CH_3$$

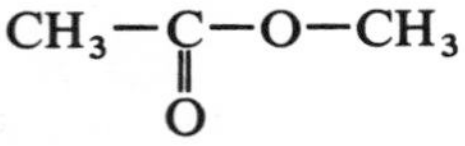

methyl acetate

SAQ 30 Which of the following statements are true and which are false?

(a) Carbon–hydrogen bonds are polar.

(b) Propanoic acid and methyl acetate are functional isomers.

(c) Geometric isomers have the same molecular formula and the same sequence of atoms.

(d) A plasticizer is the substance used to cause a monomer to form an addition polymer.

(e) Hydrogen bonds can be formed between two hydroxyl (—OH) groups and between two amino (—NH$_2$) groups, but not between a hydroxyl group and an amino group.

SAQ 31   Propan-1-ol, CH$_3$—CH$_2$—CH$_2$—OH, has a boiling temperature of 97 °C and is completely soluble in water. In contrast, its isomer methoxyethane, CH$_3$—O—CH$_2$—CH$_3$, has a boiling temperature of 11 °C and is not completely soluble in water. Explain.

SAQ 32   Draw all the structural isomers of molecular formula C$_5$H$_{10}$O that contain a carbonyl group. Distinguish between those that are ketones and those that are aldehydes.

SAQ 33   Which of the following statements are true, and which are false?

(a) DNA is an addition polymer.

(b) DNA is a heteropolymer.

(c) The sequence of bases in any one DNA molecule is the same as in any other DNA molecule.

(d) DNA molecules combine in pairs in the form of a 'double helix' held together by London forces.

(e) DNA acts as a blueprint for the polymerization of amino acids to form proteins.

9 TV NOTES: ORGANIC MOLECULES IN ACTION

The programme deals with two main themes: applications of the phenomenon of stereoisomerism and the reactions of carbon compounds. The first is illustrated by two examples: one, the development of an environmentally more sensitive method of pest control than simply to rely on insecticides; the other, the production of a chemical intermediate called glycidyl butyrate with uses in the health-care field for manufacture of, for example, the so-called 'beta-blockers' (drugs for treating heart and circulation disorders), some of which are in the top five most widely used pharmaceuticals. The second theme is illustrated by the method used to make glycidyl butyrate from simpler starting compounds.

Do not expect to understand fully all that you see in the programme until you have been able to read up to and including Section 5.3 particularly Sections 4.3 and 5.3. However, your learning of the material in these Sections will be greatly assisted by the relevant images from the programme.

10 TV NOTES: MAN-MADE MACROMOLECULES

The programme deals with polymerization and the properties of synthetic polymers. It examines three of the polymers produced on the largest scale: polyethylene, polypropylene and nylon-6,6. In each case, samples of the polymer are prepared on the laboratory scale and the mechanism of polymerization explained. In addition the programme shows the way in which polyethylene and nylon-6,6 are made on the industrial scale. The programme is linked directly with Section 7.

The programme begins with one of the most common polymers, polyethylene, or polythene. The discovery of polyethylene was quite accidental. During the 1930s, ICI began to study the effect of high pressures on chemical reactions. One such experiment involving ethylene produced a white powder with quite unique properties.

However, synthetic polymer science was in its infancy and the importance of the discovery was not realized at once. Work on the reaction was halted for over two years. When work was restarted, larger quantities of polyethylene were prepared and its excellent electrical insulation properties discovered. Polyethylene found its first application in submarine telephone cables, but when full-scale commercial production began in 1939, most of the output was diverted for use in radar.

The discovery of polyethylene illustrates two important points. First, the role of chance: both the initial observation of an unexpected product and the fact that a trace of oxygen was present adventitiously to initiate the reaction (see below) come into this category. The second point is that the experiments could only be carried out once the technological problems of working with very high pressures (up to 3 000 atm) had been solved. Now, of course, as the programme shows, such high pressures are used routinely in production, not just in research.

The polymerization of ethylene is called addition polymerization. Such polymerizations require an initiator. Oxygen, which was present in the initial experiments, does not give reproducible results, and normally other initiators are used. Di-*tertiary*-butyl peroxide, the one used in the programme, on heating, gives rise to methyl radicals, which start the reaction off:

$$CH_3-\underset{\underset{CH_3}{|}}{\overset{\overset{CH_3}{|}}{C}}-O-O-\underset{\underset{CH_3}{|}}{\overset{\overset{CH_3}{|}}{C}}-CH_3 \xrightarrow{\text{heat}} 2\,CH_3\cdot + 2\,CH_3-\underset{\underset{O}{\|}}{C}-CH_3$$

di-*tertiary*-butyl peroxide   methyl radicals   acetone

The polymerization scheme is given in Section 7.2.

Until the early 1950s, the high-pressure route was the only way of making polyethylene. However, at that time, Karl Ziegler in Germany developed a process by which ethylene could be polymerized using much lower pressures. The method involves the use of certain metallic compounds as catalysts. The resulting polymer had rather different properties: it was less flexible, had a higher melting temperature and a higher density than the high-pressure material. The severity of the conditions in the high-pressure method leads to a considerable number of branches in the polymer chain. However, the low-pressure process gives a polymer that is more like the ideal linear chain with no branches.

At about the same time, Giulio Natta developed a similar process for polymerizing propylene. Propylene cannot be polymerized by the high-pressure method. However, the low-pressure process gives a product that is similar in properties to low-pressure polyethylene, though with significant advantages in many applications. Polypropylene is not only linear, but also has a regular structure.

In contrast to the discovery of polyethylene, the discovery of nylon-6,6 by Wallace Carothers in the laboratories of the du Pont Company in the USA was the result of research directed towards the synthesis of polymeric material. Nylon-6,6 results when hexanedioic acid and hexane-1,6-diamine are reacted together. The initial product of reaction is simply a salt, called 'nylon salt':

$$H_2N-(CH_2)_6-NH_2 + HO-\underset{\underset{O}{\|}}{C}-(CH_2)_4-\underset{\underset{O}{\|}}{C}-OH$$

$$\downarrow$$

$$H_3\overset{+}{N}-(CH_2)_6-\overset{+}{N}H_3 \quad \overset{-}{O}-\underset{\underset{O}{\|}}{C}-(CH_2)_4-\underset{\underset{O}{\|}}{C}-\overset{-}{O}$$

nylon salt

(Notice that in formulae such as these the sequence of atoms in the functional groups is often inverted for clarity; for example, H_2N- rather than NH_2-.)

The nylon salt is then heated to about 300 °C and condensation takes place, with a water molecule being expelled as each amide link in the chain is formed:

$$\cdots-CH_2-\overset{+}{N}H_3 \quad \overset{-}{O}-\underset{\underset{O}{\|}}{C}-CH_2-\cdots \xrightarrow{\text{heat}}$$

$$\cdots-CH_2-NH-\underset{\underset{O}{\|}}{C}-CH_2-\cdots \ +H_2O$$

Industrially, the salt is formed in aqueous solution. The solution is concentrated from 50% to about 80%. The concentrated solution then passes to an autoclave ('big industrial pressure cooker'), where it is heated in the absence of air (to prevent oxidation) until the polymer chains are the required length. The nylon is then extruded onto a conveyor belt and broken into chips for subsequent fabrication.

OBJECTIVES FOR UNITS 17–18

After you have worked through these Units, you should be able to:

1 Explain the meaning of, and use correctly, all the terms flagged in the text.

2 Write down the Lewis structures of methane, fluoromethane, methanol, methylamine, ethane, ethylene and acetylene. (*SAQ 1*)

3 Work out the Lewis structures of other simple compounds containing fewer than ten atoms. (*ITQ 1, SAQ 2*)

4 Recognize abbreviated structural formulae in which one or more atoms have incorrectly filled valence shells. (*SAQ 3*)

5 (a) Relate the gross trends in boiling temperatures and solubilities of a series of compounds to their structural formulae, and (b) explain the solubility properties of a given compound in polar and non-polar solvents, in terms of the three main types of intermolecular forces (*ITQ 2, SAQs 4, 5, 6, 7, 9 and 31*)

6 Given a series of structural formulae, identify those that are members of a homologous series, structural isomers (functional isomers, skeletal isomers and position isomers), and stereoisomers (geometric isomers and optical isomers). (*ITQs 3, 4 and 5, SAQs 8, 10, 12, 14, 15, 16, 17 and 18*)

7 Recognize the functional groups characteristic of the homologous series of alkenes, alkynes, alcohols, ethers, aldehydes, ketones, carboxylic acids, acid chlorides, amides, esters and amines. (*ITQs 9 and 10, SAQs 6 and 13*)

8 Classify a given chemical transformation as oxidation, reduction, addition, condensation (ester formation or amide formation) or hydrolysis. (*SAQ 23*)

9 Write down or select from a series of structural formulae (a) the product that would be formed from a given reactant, or (b) the reactant that would give rise to a given product, by one of the transformations listed in Objective 8. (*ITQ 7 and SAQs 24 and 27*)

10   Write down all the structural isomers containing a particular functional group for a given molecular formula with up to six carbon atoms. (*ITQ 3, SAQs 11, 12, 16, 18 and 32*)

11   Classify any simple molecule as being chiral or non-chiral. (*SAQs 19, 20 and 21*)

12   Distinguish observations or analogies which could in principle reflect the influence of molecular chirality from those that could not. (*SAQs 21 and 22*)

13   Calculate the specific rotation of an optically active substance from the observed angle of rotation of plane-polarized light, or vice versa, given other necessary data. (*ITQs 6 and 8*)

14   Recognize a given molecular structure as (a) an initiator, (b) an addition polymer, (c) a condensation polymer, (d) a monomer for addition polymerization, and (e) a monomer for condensation polymerization. (*SAQs 27 and 28*)

15   Outline the sequence of reactions involved in radical-initiated addition polymerization and in condensation polymerization. (*SAQs 26 and 27*)

16   Predict the polymer that would result from a given monomer(s), or deduce the monomer(s) that would give rise to a given polymer. (*SAQs 25, 27 and 29*)

17   Relate some of the physical properties of an addition or condensation polymer to its molecular structure. (*SAQ 29*)

18   (a) Recognize the structure of a section of a polypeptide, protein, or DNA molecule and (b) state the main relationship between DNA and proteins. (*SAQ 33*)

ITQ ANSWERS AND COMMENTS

ITQ 1   Nitrogen is in Group V of the Periodic Table, oxygen is in Group VI, chlorine and bromine are in Group VII. So chlorine and bromine behave like fluorine: each needs just one more electron to achieve the electronic configuration of the nearest noble gas. Oxygen and nitrogen, on the other hand, need two and three electrons, respectively. So they cannot form compounds with structural formulae analogous to that of fluoromethane, since that would leave them short of electrons: oxygen would have a share of seven and nitrogen of six, instead of eight.

ITQ 2   The use of an organic solvent implies that the soiling matter must be largely 'hydrocarbon-like'— remember the rule of thumb 'like dissolves like'. As you know from the experiment for Units 13–14, trichloroethane readily dissolves covalent substances.

ITQ 3   (a) The structures of the aldehydes and ketones that have the molecular formula C_4H_8O are **1, 2** and **3**. The first step is to write down all the possible carbon skeletons. As usual with four carbons, there are just two:

C—C—C—C   and   C—C—C
                         |
                         C

Next, place the carbonyl group oxygen atom in as many different positions as possible (remember the carbon atom is already in place):

C—C—C—C

1 $CH_3{-}CH_2{-}CH_2{-}CH{=}O$ **2** $CH_3{-}CH_2{-}C{-}CH_3$
                                                               ‖
                                                               O

C—C—C
    |
    C
    ↓
3 $CH_3{-}CH{-}CH{=}O$
              |
              CH_3

Note that, with the branched skeleton, it is not possible to have a tertiary carbon (one with three carbons attached) which is part of a carbonyl group, so there are just three possibilities.

(b) Using butanal (structure **1**) as a reference, **2** is a functional isomer, and **3** is a skeletal isomer.

(Remember, aldehydes and ketones have *different* functional groups.)

ITQ 4   Since all three have different functional groups from propanal, they are all functional isomers. Within the group, however, each is a position isomer of any other.

ITQ 5 There are two. The left-hand double bond of penta-1,3-diene has different groups at both ends, whereas the right-hand double bond has two identical atoms (H) at one end. So while there can be a *cis* and *trans* relationship for the groups attached to the left-hand double bond, this is not the case for the right-hand one. (a) and (c) are the *trans* and *cis* isomers, respectively; (b) is simply structure (a) with one end of the molecule rotated about the central C—C single bond.

The same would be true for 3-methylpenta-1,3-diene (below), although now the left-hand double bond no longer has two hydrogens attached. In this case, whether an isomer is called *cis* or *trans* is determined by the *larger* of the two groups at either end:

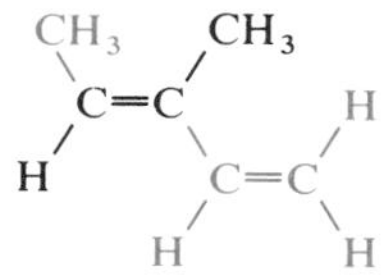

trans-3-methylpenta-1,3-diene

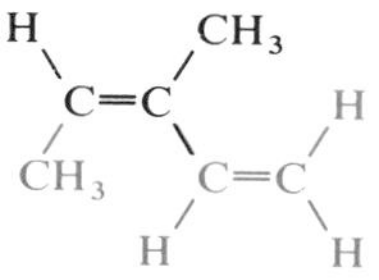

cis-3-methylpenta-1,3-diene

ITQ 6 The observed rotation α would be 0.139°; the front polarizer would need to be rotated in an anticlockwise direction, by definition, since this is the (−) isomer.

Using the equation for specific rotation:

$$[\alpha]_D = \frac{\alpha}{lc}$$

which rearranged gives

$$\alpha = [\alpha]_D lc$$

Remember l is in decimetres and c in $g\,cm^{-3}$. So, in this example, $l = 0.1$ and $c = 0.1$, which, with a value of 13.9° for $[\alpha]_D$, gives

$$\alpha = 13.9 \times 0.1 \times 0.1°$$
$$= 0.139°$$

So this diluted sample and a relatively short path length would give a small rotation. But measurement of such small rotations is well within the capabilities of modern automatic polarimeters of the type demonstrated in the TV programme 'Organic molecules in action'.

ITQ 7 The reactions involved are as follows:

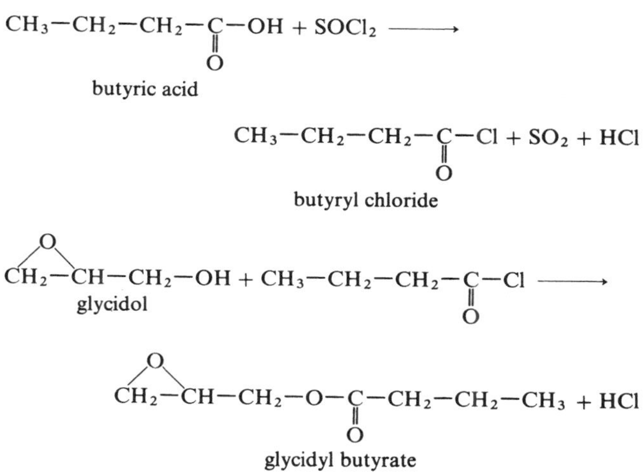

ITQ 8 Using the equation for the specific rotation, the expected angle of rotation for pure (−)glycidyl butyrate is given as follows:

$$\alpha = -29 \times 0.1 \times 0.1°$$
$$= -0.29°$$

Since this was the measured angle, the separation process must have been essentially 100% successful.

ITQ 9 The functional groups in question are as follows:

alkenes	C=C	(see Section 4.1)
alkynes	C≡C	(see Section 4.1)
fluoroalkanes	C—F	(see Section 3.1)
aldehydes	—CH=O	(see Section 4.1)
ketones	C—C—C || O	(see Section 4.1)

*Fluoro*alkanes are one type of *halo*alkane, R—Hal, where Hal = F, Cl, Br or I.

ITQ 10 Butan-1-ol and 2-methylpropan-1-ol are both primary alcohols (they each have a —CH$_2$—OH group); butan-2-ol is a secondary alcohol (it has a C—CH—OH group); 2-methylpropan-2-ol is a tertiary alcohol (it has a C—C—OH group).

SAQ ANSWERS AND COMMENTS

SAQ 1 The Lewis structures of methane and methanol are as shown below.

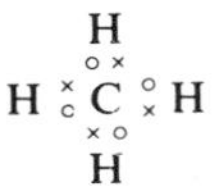

methane 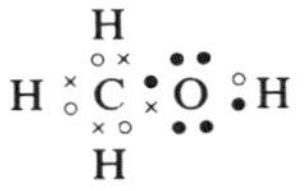   methanol

SAQ 2 (a) The Lewis structure of fluoromethylamine, $F-CH_2-NH_2$, can be worked out by extension from the Lewis structures of fluoromethane, CH_3-F, and methylamine, CH_3-NH_2, and is as shown below.

(b) The structural formula of fluoromethylamine can then be deduced from its Lewis structure by replacing each bonding pair of electrons by a line and not showing the non-bonding electron pairs explicitly.

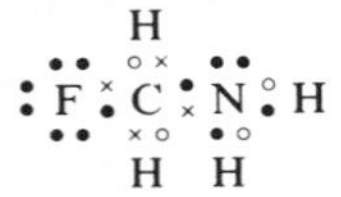

Lewis structure of fluoromethylamine

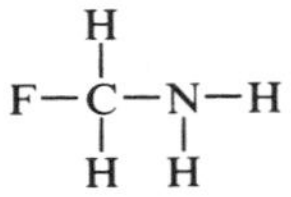

structural formula of fluoromethylamine

SAQ 3 All the atoms in formulae (a) and (d) have correctly filled valence shells. However, formulae (b) and (c) do not. In formula (b), nitrogen has ten electrons—two too many (four bonding pairs, one non-bonding pair). In formula (c), carbon has only six electrons—two too few (three bonding pairs).

The easiest way to tackle this is to look at the number of bonds to each atom using Table 1 to remind you of the valencies. Clearly, then, in (b) the carbon atom has a valency of 4, the hydrogen and fluorine atoms each have a valency of 1, but the nitrogen atom apparently has a valency of 4. In contrast, in (c), the carbon atom apparently has a valency of 3.

SAQ 4 Yes, the order of boiling temperatures is consistent with the discussion of intermolecular forces in Section 2.2. The dipole–dipole forces predominate.

Bromine and iodine monochloride have roughly equal relative molecular masses. So if the London forces alone were involved, they should have very similar boiling temperatures. However, bromine should have no permanent dipole; iodine monochloride, on the other hand, will have a permanent dipole because of the difference in electronegativity between iodine and chlorine (Units 13–14). This means that dipole–dipole attraction will contribute to the intermolecular forces in iodine monochloride, leading to a higher boiling temperature than bromine, in agreement with the values given.

SAQ 5 (a) The increase in relative molecular mass on going down the series H_2S, H_2Se, H_2Te would lead to a corresponding increase in London forces between the molecules in each case. This then accounts for the order of boiling temperatures given.

(b) On the basis of London forces alone, the value for water is anomalously high. This is the result of the extensive hydrogen-bonding possible between H_2O molecules but not between molecules of the other three hydrides.

You may be interested to know that hydrogen-bonding accounts for many of the apparently anomalous properties of water. For example, solid water (ice) is less dense than liquid water (ice floats on water) because of the extensive network of hydrogen bonds that create a very 'open' structure, whereas most solids are more dense than their liquid form. This is of immense importance for the viability of life in ponds and rivers during winter.

SAQ 6 (a) False; (b) true; (c) true; (d) false; (e) true.

(a) Hydrogen atoms attached to oxygen atoms form stronger hydrogen bonds than those attached to nitrogen atoms. The order of strength of hydrogen bonds is $O-H\text{------}O$ strongest, $O-H\text{------}N$ and $N-H\text{------}O$ next strongest, and $N-H\text{------}N$ least strong. (None the less, these latter hydrogen bonds are of immense importance to life; see Section 7.5.)

(b) London forces arise from the instantaneous dipoles caused by the displacement of the centre of negative charge (due to the electrons) from the centre of positive charge (due to the nuclei) and so are present between all molecules.

(c) The division into an active functional group and an inactive hydrocarbon group means that hydrocarbons such as methane are 'inactive' in this context i.e. do not possess a functional group.

(d) The molecular formula of methanol is CH_4O; CH_3-OH is the abbreviated structural formula.

(e) The definition of a halocarbon is a compound with molecules that contain carbon and one or more halogens (Group VII elements) with or without hydrogen, and no other elements.

SAQ 7 Iodomethane has a higher molecular mass than bromomethane, and so the London forces between the molecules are greater. The expectation on this basis would be, therefore, that CH_3I should have the higher boiling temperature. In contrast, the higher electronegativity of bromine over iodine should lead to the $C-Br$ bond being more polar than the $C-I$ bond, and hence there should be stronger dipole–dipole forces. Hydrogen bonding is not possible since there are no hydrogen atoms attached to oxygen or nitrogen. The observed relative boiling temperatures must therefore mean that the London forces predominate over the dipole–dipole forces.

SAQ 8 1 and 3; 2 and 7; 5 and 8. The members of each pair differ from one another by a whole number of $-CH_2-$ groups.

SAQ 9 The presence of the single –OH group in the hexadecan-1-ol molecule compared with the 16 –CH_2– groups means that the hydrogen bonding plays only a small part in the intermolecular forces. Consequently, the large hexadecan-1-ol molecule is unable to compensate sufficiently for the disruption of a large number of hydrogen bonds between the methanol molecules in pure methanol. Since the London forces between hexadecan-1-ol molecules are dominant, these forces are readily compensated by similar forces between heptane molecules and the hexadecan-1-ol molecules.

SAQ 10 X1 and Y1: B; X2 and Y2: E; X3 and Y3: F; X4 and Y4: A; X5 and Y5: C; X6 and Y6: D.

X1 and Y1 have the same skeleton and the same functional group, but at a different position.

X2 and Y2 are identical. (Make up models if you are not convinced of this.)

X3 and Y3 have different molecular formulae, so they are not isomers, and different functional groups so they cannot be members of the same homologous series.

X4 and Y4 are very similar (the same functional group located in a similar position within the molecule) but differ by one –CH_2– group.

X5 and Y5 have the same molecular formula but different functional groups.

X6 and Y6 have the same molecular formula but different carbon skeletons.

SAQ 11 The structural isomers with molecular formula C_5H_{12} are (a), (b) and (c) below.

(a) $CH_3-CH_2-CH_2-CH_2-CH_3$

(b) $CH_3-CH_2-\underset{\underset{CH_3}{|}}{CH}-CH_3$

(c) $CH_3-\underset{\underset{CH_3}{|}}{\overset{\overset{CH_3}{|}}{C}}-CH_3$

There are only three different C_5H_{12} alkanes. If you have more, then some of your structures must be identical even though they look different; for example:

$CH_3-CH_2-CH_2-\underset{\underset{CH_3}{|}}{CH_2}$ is the same as (a)

$CH_3-\underset{\underset{CH_3}{|}}{CH}-CH_2-CH_3$ is the same as (b)

SAQ 12 The structural isomers with molecular formula C_4H_9F are the compounds (a)–(d).

Because the fluorine atom is monovalent, there cannot be any functional isomers: the fluorine atom can only be attached to one carbon atom. The first thing to do, then, is to write down all the possible carbon skeletons; these are the same as for the alcohols with four carbon atoms:

$C-C-C-C$ and $C-\underset{\underset{C}{|}}{C}-C$

If you have any others then they must be identical with one of the two above. The next step is to locate the position that the fluorine atom can occupy. There are four in all that are different, two for each skeleton:

$$C-C-C-C$$

(a) $CH_3-CH_2-CH_2-CH_2F$ (b) $CH_3-CH_2-CHF-CH_3$

$$C-C-C$$
$$\overset{\overset{}{|}}{C}$$

(c) $CH_3-\underset{\underset{CH_3}{|}}{CH}-CH_2F$ (d) $CH_3-\underset{\underset{CH_3}{|}}{CF}-CH_3$

If you have any others they must just be the same structures written differently. For example:

$CH_3-CH_2-CHF-CH_3$ and $CH_3-CHF-CH_2-CH_3$ are identical; and $CH_3-\underset{\underset{CH_3}{|}}{CH}-CH_2F$ and $CH_3-\underset{\underset{CH_2F}{|}}{CH}-CH_3$ are identical.

So (a) and (b) are position isomers, as are (c) and (d); (a) and (c) or (a) and (d) are skeletal isomers, as are (b) and (c) or (b) and (d).

SAQ 13 1: F; 2: E; 3: B; 4: H; 5: C; 6: G.

Structure 1 has a –$CH=O$ group, the functional group of the aldehydes.

Structure 2 has an –NH_2 group, the functional group of the alkylamines.

Structure 3 has a $C=C$ group, so is an alkene.

Structure 4 has a carboxyl group, so is a carboxylic acid.

Structure 5 has a $C\equiv C$ group, so is an alkyne.

Structure 6 has a carbonyl group attached to a carbon atom on each side, so is a ketone.

SAQ 14 Since the two molecules have the same functional group, they are not functional isomers. Since the carbon skeleton is the same in both, they are not skeletal isomers. They only differ in the position of the functional group, so they are position isomers. (Note that they are different from ethers in this regard, because with ethers the oxygen atom is part of the backbone, whereas with ketones it is the carbon atom of the carbonyl group that is involved.)

SAQ 15 X1 and Y1: B; X2 and Y2: A; X3 and Y3: C; X4 and Y4: E; X5 and Y5: D.

X1 and Y1 have the same molecular formula, but a different sequence of atoms.

The molecular formulae of X2 and Y2 differ by –CH_2–, and they have the same functional group.

X3 and Y3 have the same sequence of atoms, but different geometry about the $C=C$ double bond. Note that merely turning the formula over does not alter it.

X4 and Y4 have different molecular formulae that do not differ by an integral number of $-CH_2-$ groups.

Y5 is simply X5 turned over and rotated.

SAQ 16 The first stage is to draw the possible carbon skeletons, then put in the double bond, then place the chlorine atom. With three carbon atoms there is only one skeleton possible and one position for the double bond.

$$C-C-C \rightarrow C-C=C$$

(a) $Cl-CH_2-CH=CH_2$

(b) $CH_3-\underset{\underset{Cl}{|}}{C}=CH_2$

(c) $\underset{\underset{H}{|}}{CH_3}\underset{}{C}=\underset{\underset{H}{|}}{C}\overset{Cl}{}$ (c) cis

(d) $\underset{\underset{H}{|}}{CH_3}\underset{}{C}=\underset{\underset{Cl}{|}}{C}\overset{H}{}$

(a), (b) and either (c) or (d) are structural isomers (in fact position isomers) of one another; (c) and (d) are geometric isomers, with (c) being the *cis* isomer and (d) the *trans*.

SAQ 17 With esters, as with ethers, an oxygen atom is part of the backbone. For $C_3H_6O_2$ there are three possibilities in all.

(a) $CH_3-CH_2-\underset{\underset{O}{\|}}{C}-OH$ (b) $CH_3-\underset{\underset{O}{\|}}{C}-O-CH_3$

(c) $H-\underset{\underset{O}{\|}}{C}-O-CH_2-CH_3$

Note that (a) and (c) are different because of the unsymmetrical nature of the ester grouping. (a) is an acid while (b) and (c) are esters. So (a) is a functional isomer of (b) or (c), while (b) and (c) are skeletal isomers.

SAQ 18 There are 11 possible structures, including three pairs of geometric isomers.

We follow the same type of strategy as in SAQ 16.

Draw the carbon skeletons:

$$C-C-C-C \quad \text{and} \quad C-\underset{\underset{C}{|}}{C}-C$$

Put in the double bonds:

(1) $C-C-C=C$ (2) $C-C=C-C$

(3) $C-\underset{\underset{C}{|}}{C}=C$

Place the $-OH$ groups:

1(a) $CH_3-CH_2-CH=CH-OH$ (*cis* or *trans*)

1(b) $CH_3-CH_2-\underset{\underset{OH}{|}}{C}=CH_2$

1(c) $CH_3-\underset{\underset{OH}{|}}{CH}-CH=CH_2$

1(d) $HO-CH_2-CH_2-CH=CH_2$

2(a) $CH_3-CH=CH-CH_2-OH$ (*cis* or *trans*)

2(b) $CH_3-CH=\underset{\underset{OH}{|}}{C}-CH_3$ (*cis* or *trans*)

3(a) $CH_3-\underset{\underset{CH_3}{|}}{C}=CH-OH$

3(b) $CH_3-\underset{\underset{CH_2-OH}{|}}{C}=CH_2$

Drawing out the structures of the *cis* and *trans* isomers in full:

$$\underset{\underset{H}{} \quad \underset{H}{}}{CH_3-CH_2} \underset{}{C}=C \overset{OH}{}$$
cis-1(a)

$$CH_3-CH_2 \quad H$$
$$C=C$$
$$H \quad OH$$
trans-1(a)

$$CH_3 \quad CH_2-OH$$
$$C=C$$
$$H \quad H$$
cis-2(a)

$$CH_3 \quad H$$
$$C=C$$
$$H \quad CH_2-OH$$
trans-2(a)

$$H \quad OH$$
$$C=C$$
$$CH_3 \quad CH_3$$
cis-2(b)

$$H \quad CH_3$$
$$C=C$$
$$CH_3 \quad OH$$
trans-2(b)

Note that for *cis*- and *trans*-2(b), which is called *cis* and which *trans* is determined by the larger group of the pair at each end, here the $-CH_3$ group.

SAQ 19 (a) is non-chiral since a model and its mirror image can be superimposed; (b) is chiral since a model and its mirror image cannot be superimposed; (c) is non-chiral but (d) is chiral. (Remember you can rotate one end of (c) or (d) relative to the other.) If you are still unconvinced, but have attempted this question by making three-dimensional drawings, try making up models of each of the structures and their mirror images. You will find that only for (b) and (d) are they not superimposable.

SAQ 20 (a) is non-chiral; it has only two different types of atom attached to the carbon atom.

(b) is chiral; the left-hand atom has only two different types of atom or group attached ($-H$ and $-CHBrCl$), but the right-hand carbon atom has four different atoms or groups ($-CH_3$, $-H$, $-Br$ and $-Cl$).

(c) is chiral; the third carbon from the left is a chiral centre, since it has four different groups attached ($-CH_2-CH_3$, $-H$, $-OH$ and $-CH_3$).

(d) is non-chiral; each carbon atom has only three different groups attached ($-H$, $-F$ and $-CH_2F$, and $-H$, $-F$ and $-CHF_2$).

(e) is chiral; the second carbon from the left is a chiral centre, since it has four different groups attached:

$$-CH_3, -H, -OH \text{ and } -\overset{\displaystyle O}{\underset{\displaystyle \|}{C}}-OH$$

(f) is chiral; the third carbon atom from the left is a chiral centre, since it has four different groups attached ($-CH_2-CH_3$, $-H$, $-CH_3$ and $-CH_2-CH_2-CH_3$). Note that you have to look at the *whole* of the group attached; the fact that both $-CH_2-CH_3$ and $-CH_2-CH_2-CH_3$ have $-CH_2-$ groups attached to the carbon atom in question does not mean that they can be treated as the same. If you are still in doubt, make up models and try the mirror-image test.

SAQ 21 The central carbon atom in 4-methylheptan-3-one is a chiral centre because it has four different groups attached ($-CH_2-CH_2-CH_3$, $-H$, $-CH_3$ and $-\overset{\displaystyle O}{\underset{\displaystyle \|}{C}}-CH_2-CH_3$). Given that insects can distinguish geometric isomers (Section 4.3) and given that living systems can differentiate other optical isomers, the chances of an insect distinguishing the two optical isomers in this case are high. In fact, careful tests show the (+) isomer to be approximately 100 times more effective as an alarm pheromone than the (−) isomer, pointing to a chiral receptor site.

SAQ 22 Only (c), (d) and (e) could be correct experimental observations, for the reasons given below.

(a) Not possible. Optical isomers only show different behaviour when they interact with something which itself is chiral. Water molecules are not chiral (since a model and its mirror image can be superimposed).

(b) Not possible. Acetic acid is non-chiral, so racemic butan-2-ol would give racemic 2-butyl acetate.

(c) Possible. The product of reaction of (+)butan-2-ol with acetic acid will certainly be optically active and the part of the ester derived from the alcohol will retain the same configuration. However, it is not possible to say, without making the measurement, whether it will rotate the plane of polarized light clockwise or anticlockwise; even though (+)butan-2-ol is used, the product could be the (−) isomer of the ester.

(d) Possible. Living systems are chiral and can differentiate other chiral substances, so the chances are quite high that a chiral receptor site would be involved in this instance also. In fact, (−)methadone is considerably more effective than (+)methadone.

(e) Possible (and in fact true). Optical isomers have the same physical properties except when a chiral environment or agent is involved.

SAQ 23 1: C; 2: D; 3: A; 4: B *and* C; 5: D; 6: E.

1 This involves the addition of the HBr molecule with the formation of two new bonds, one to each of the carbon atoms of the double bond.

2 This involves the linking (condensation) of two molecules with the expulsion of an HCl molecule.

3 This is the oxidation of a primary alcohol to a carboxylic acid which involves both the addition of oxygen and the removal of hydrogen.

4 This involves the addition reaction of hydrogen to a triple bond—it is therefore both a reduction *and* an addition reaction.

5 This involves the linking (condensation) of two molecules with the expulsion of an H_2O molecule.

6 In order to see that this is hydrolysis, you have to recall that acetic acid will form a salt with NaOH and that NaOH is present as an aqueous solution.

SAQ 24 Reaction 1: (b); reaction 2: (a); reaction 3: (b); reaction 4: (a) or (c).

1 This reaction is a reduction of a ketone to a secondary alcohol: (a) involves the removal of the carbonyl oxygen and formation of a carbon–carbon double bond; (c) is a tertiary alcohol.

2 This reaction involves the reduction of an alkyne to a *trans*-alkene: (b) is the *cis*-alkene; (c) is the fully-reduced product.

3 This reaction is a condensation to give an ester: (a) would be the product from 2-methylpropanoyl chloride and methanol; (c) is a ketone.

$$CH_3-\underset{\displaystyle \underset{\displaystyle CH_3}{|}}{CH}-\overset{\displaystyle O}{\overset{\displaystyle \|}{C}}-Cl \qquad\qquad CH_3-OH$$

2-methylpropanoyl chloride   methanol

4 The product is either (a) or (c) depending on the conditions. The reaction involves the oxidation of a primary alcohol first to an aldehyde (a), and possibly further to a carboxylic acid (c); (b) is a ketone with a different carbon skeleton.

SAQ 25 The repeating unit is

$$-\underset{\displaystyle \underset{\displaystyle O-CH_3}{\underset{\displaystyle |}{\underset{\displaystyle C=O}{\underset{\displaystyle |}{}}}}}{\overset{\displaystyle \overset{\displaystyle CH_3}{|}}{C}}-CH_2- \qquad \text{or} \qquad -CH_2-\underset{\displaystyle \underset{\displaystyle O-CH_3}{\underset{\displaystyle |}{\underset{\displaystyle C=O}{\underset{\displaystyle |}{}}}}}{\overset{\displaystyle \overset{\displaystyle CH_3}{|}}{C}}-$$

So the monomer is

$$CH_2=C\overset{\displaystyle CH_3}{\underset{\displaystyle \underset{\displaystyle O}{\overset{\displaystyle \|}{C}}-O-CH_3}{}}$$

The polymer is, in fact, poly(methyl methacrylate), known more commonly as Perspex or Plexiglass.

SAQ 26 The first stage is formation of radicals from the initiator, followed by reaction with a monomer molecule (stages 2 and 3):

$$Ph-\underset{\underset{O}{\|}}{C}-O-O-\underset{\underset{O}{\|}}{C}-Ph \xrightarrow{\text{heat or light}} 2Ph-\underset{\underset{O}{\|}}{C}-O\cdot$$

$$Ph-\underset{\underset{O}{\|}}{C}-O\cdot \longrightarrow Ph\cdot + CO_2$$

$$\left.\begin{array}{c}\end{array}\right\} \tag{1}$$

$$Ph\cdot + CH_2=CH-Cl \longrightarrow Ph-CH_2-\dot{C}HCl \tag{2}$$

$$Ph-CH_2-\dot{C}HCl + CH_2=CH-Cl$$
$$\longrightarrow Ph-CH_2-CHCl-CH_2-\dot{C}HCl \tag{3}$$

The polymer is, in fact, poly(vinyl chloride), or PVC.

SAQ 27 Statement (a): D; statement (b): C; statement (c): E.

(a) An addition polymerization is one that produces a polymer with the same ratio of atoms of constituent elements as the monomer (neglecting the small contribution to the formula made by groups at the ends of the chain, which may have come from initiator molecules). Addition polymers can be formed in ways other than through radical initiation, for example, via Ziegler–Natta catalysis.

(b) Condensation polymers do not necessarily involve two reactants. For example, glycine can be made to condense with itself to form the protein-type polyamide, polyglycine.

(c) X can condense with Y to form nylon-3,5, and Z can condense with itself to form a protein-type polyamide, nylon-3. However, X could only condense with two molecules of Z before reaction ceased, since, though the amino groups would condense with the carboxyl group of Z, the product of that reaction would have amino groups at both ends, and hence could not react with more X.

$$NH_2-(CH_2)_3-NH_2 + 2\ NH_2-(CH_2)_3-\underset{\underset{O}{\|}}{C}-OH \rightsquigarrow$$

$$NH_2-(CH_2)_3-\underset{\underset{O}{\|}}{C}-NH-(CH_2)_3-NH-\underset{\underset{O}{\|}}{C}-(CH_2)_3-NH_2 + 2H_2O$$

SAQ 28 A: addition polymer (polystyrene); B: condensation polymer (nylon-6); C: initiator (contains an O—O bond); D: monomer (decanedioic acid) for condensation polymerization (needs another monomer to react with, for example, $NH_2-(CH_2)_6-NH_2$); E: monomer (vinylidene chloride) for addition polymerization; F: addition polymer (Teflon or PTFE).

SAQ 29 (a) The repeating unit is $\quad -CH-CH_2-\quad$ so the monomer is $CH_2=CH-C\equiv N$. $\underset{\underset{C\equiv N}{|}}{}$

(b) The polymer does not contain any hydrogen atoms attached to an oxygen or a nitrogen atom, so there cannot be any hydrogen bonding. However, the $C\equiv N$ bond is polar (the electronegativities of carbon and nitrogen are different) so there are dipole–dipole forces between the chains. Consequently, Orlon has good fibre-forming properties for the same reason that Tery-

lene does. The fact that there are relatively few crystallites indicates that a large proportion of the chains are randomly orientated, so the contribution from London forces is likely to be smaller than it is, for example, in polypropylene.

SAQ 30 Statements (b) and (c) are true; statements (a), (d) and (e) are false.

(a) Carbon and hydrogen have similar electronegativities, so carbon–hydrogen bonds cannot be polar.

(b) They have the same molecular formula, $C_3H_6O_2$, and have different functional groups: one is a carboxylic acid, the other is an ester. As such they are not simply positional isomers.

(c) See Section 4.2.

(d) An initiator is the substance that causes a monomer to form an addition polymer. A plasticizer is the substance used to make a rigid polymer, such as PVC, pliable.

(e) A hydrogen bond can be formed between any two molecules that have the groups X—H and Y, respectively, where X and Y are elements of high electronegativity, frequently O or N. So the most usual hydrogen bonds are one of the following types:

$$O-H\text{------}O, \quad O-H\text{------}N, \quad N-H\text{------}O, \quad N-H\text{------}N.$$

SAQ 31 Molecules of propan-1-ol contain hydroxyl groups that can hydrogen bond to one another. By contrast, molecules of its functional isomer, methoxyethane, do not. So, although their relative molecular masses are the same (and hence the London dispersion forces are very similar), propan-1-ol boils at a temperature considerably higher than does methoxyethane.

Similarly, the extensive hydrogen-bonding that can take place on a reciprocal basis between molecules of propan-1-ol and molecules of water compensates adequately for the disruption of the hydrogen bonds in pure water.

By contrast, molecules of methoxyethane can only act as the acceptor of a hydrogen bond, not the donor, since they contain no hydroxyl groups. Consequently, methoxyethane is only partially soluble in water.

SAQ 32 The simplest way to tackle this question is to start with the functional group and see what possible hydrocarbon skeletons there are. There are four aldehydes and three ketones.

aldehydes

$$CH_3-CH_2-CH_2-CH_2-CH=O$$

$$CH_3-CH_2-\underset{\underset{CH_3}{|}}{CH}-CH=O$$

$$CH_3-\underset{\underset{CH_3}{|}}{CH}-CH_2-CH=O$$

$$CH_3-\underset{\underset{CH_3}{|}}{\overset{\overset{CH_3}{|}}{C}}-CH=O$$

ketones

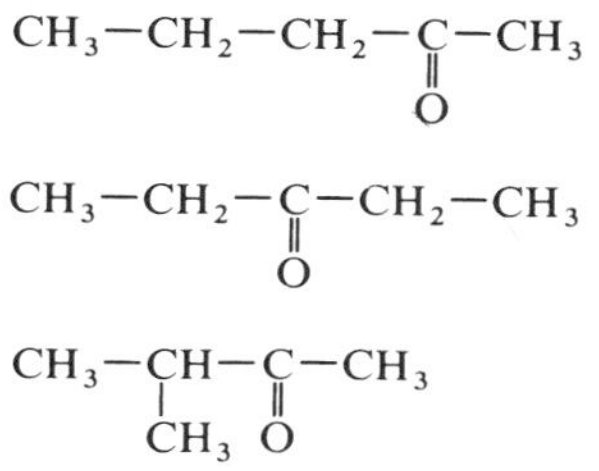

$$CH_3-CH_2-CH_2-\underset{\underset{O}{\|}}{C}-CH_3$$

$$CH_3-CH_2-\underset{\underset{O}{\|}}{C}-CH_2-CH_3$$

$$CH_3-\underset{\underset{CH_3}{|}}{CH}-\underset{\underset{O}{\|}}{C}-CH_3$$

You might have spotted that this is exactly analogous to the number of 4-carbon alcohols and ethers (four and three, respectively, see Section 3.3), with the oxygen atom replaced by a carbonyl group).

SAQ 33 (a) False; (b) true; (c) false; (d) false; (e) true.

(a) DNA is a condensation polymer (see Section 7.5).

(b) DNA is made up of four different monomers, each consisting of a phosphate group, a deoxyribose group, and one of the four bases adenine, guanine, thymine or cytosine (see Section 7.5).

(c) DNA exists as a large variety of types. The sequence of bases in any particular molecule will be the same as that in another molecule of the same type, but different from that in a molecule of another type (see Section 7.5).

(d) DNA molecules do combine in (complementary) pairs in the form of a double helix, but this is held together by hydrogen bonds, not London forces (see Section 7.5).

(e) As you will learn in the later biology Units, DNA has a number of biological functions, but controlling the polymerization of amino acids to form proteins is among the most important (see Section 7.5).

APPENDIX 1: LIST OF STEREOSLIDES

Filmstrip 1

1 Model of methane showing its tetrahedral shape.
2 Model of methane looking along a line bisecting one of the H—C—H angles.
3 Model of ethane with the C—H bonds attached to one carbon atom in line with the C—H bonds attached to the other carbon atom.
4 Model of ethane with one end (CH$_3$— group) rotated through 60° relative to the other end (CH$_3$— group) when compared with stereoslide 3.
5 Four models of CH$_3$F in different orientations.
6 Model of 1-fluoropropane.
7 Model of 2-fluoropropane.
8 Model of ethylene.
9 Models of *cis*- and *trans*-but-2-ene.

Filmstrip 2

10 Model of *cis*-β-farnesene.
11 Model of *trans*-β-farnesene.
12 Models of the two optical isomers of CHBrClI.
13 Models showing two mirror-image conformations of 1-bromo-2-chloroethane.
14 Model of (+)butan-2-ol.
15 Model of (−)butan-2-ol.
16 Model of (+)glycidol.
17 Model of (−)glycidol.
18 Model of (−)glycidyl butyrate.

APPENDIX II: LIST OF CHEMICAL NAMES AND STRUCTURES

Acetaldehyde   Older name for ethanal, $CH_3-CH=O$.

Acetic acid   Older name for ethanoic acid, $CH_3-\overset{\displaystyle O}{\underset{\displaystyle \|}{C}}-OH$.

The key ingredient in vinegar.

Acetone   The older name for propanone, $CH_3-\overset{\displaystyle O}{\underset{\displaystyle \|}{C}}-CH_3$.

Used as a general-purpose solvent in industry and as nail-varnish remover.

Acetyl chloride $CH_3-\overset{\displaystyle O}{\underset{\displaystyle \|}{C}}-Cl$

Acetylene   Older name for ethyne, $HC\equiv CH$.
Used as a fuel with pure oxygen in the oxy-acetylene torch.

Adipic acid   Older name for hexanedioic acid, $HO-\overset{\displaystyle O}{\underset{\displaystyle \|}{C}}-(CH_2)_4-\overset{\displaystyle O}{\underset{\displaystyle \|}{C}}-OH$

One of the two monomers used for making nylon-6,6.

(+)Alanine $NH_2-\overset{\displaystyle CH_3}{\underset{\displaystyle}{CH}}-\overset{\displaystyle O}{\underset{\displaystyle \|}{C}}-OH$

A naturally occurring amino acid; it has the L configuration.

Aniline $Ph-NH_2$ (Ph = phenyl group, C_6H_5)
Widely used as a chemical intermediate particularly in the manufacture of dyes.

BCF   Abbreviation for bromochlorodifluoromethane.

Bromochlorodifluoromethane $CBrClF_2$
Used in fire extinguishers for e.g. petrol fires in cars.

Bromomethane CH_3-Br

Butanal $CH_3-CH_2-CH_2-CH=O$

Butan-1-amine   Systematic name for *n*-butylamine.

Butane $CH_3-CH_2-CH_2-CH_3$
Used in liquefied form as a portable fuel in (for example) camping stoves.

Butan-1-ol   Systematic name for *n*-butyl alcohol, $CH_3-CH_2-CH_2-CH_2-OH$.

Butan-2-ol   Systematic name for *sec*-butyl alcohol, $CH_3-CH_2-\underset{\displaystyle OH}{\underset{\displaystyle |}{CH}}-CH_3$.

But-1-ene $CH_3-CH_2-CH=CH_2$

But-2-ene $CH_3-CH=CH-CH_3$

cis-But-2-ene

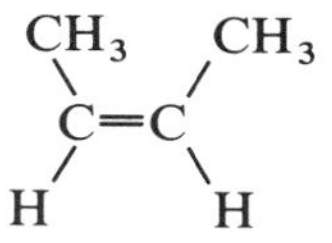

$$CH_3 \quad\quad CH_3$$
$$\text{C=C}$$
$$H \quad\quad\quad H$$

trans-But-2-ene

$$CH_3 \quad\quad H$$
$$\text{C=C}$$
$$H \quad\quad\quad CH_3$$

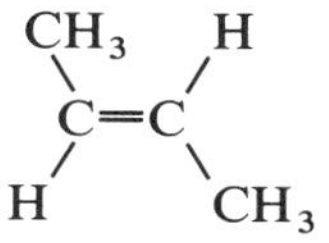

iso-Butyl alcohol   Older name for 2-methylpropan-1-ol.

n-Butyl alcohol   Older name for butan-1-ol.

sec-Butyl alcohol   Older name for butan-2-ol.

tert-Butyl alcohol   Older name for 2-methylpropan-2-ol.

n-Butylamine   Older name for butan-1-amine, $CH_3-(CH_2)_3-NH_2$.

But-1-yne $CH_3-CH_2-C{\equiv}CH$

Butyryl chloride $CH_3-CH_2-CH_2-\underset{\underset{O}{\|}}{C}-Cl$

(+)Carvone   A natural oil found in caraway.

(−)Carvone   A natural oil found in mint.

Chlorodifluoromethane   Systematic name for Freon 22, $CHClF_2$.

Chloromethane CH_3-Cl

Decan-1-amine   Systematic name for n-decylamine.

Decane $CH_3-(CH_2)_8-CH_3$

Decanoic acid $CH_3-(CH_2)_8-\underset{\underset{O}{\|}}{C}-OH$

n-Decylamine   Older name for decan-1-amine, $CH_3-(CH_2)_9-NH_2$.

Dichlorodifluoromethane   Systematic name for Freon 12, CCl_2F_2.

Dichlorofluoromethane $CHCl_2F$
The first halocarbon to be made; from its discovery sprang the huge industry devoted to the production of halocarbons for use as aerosol propellants, refrigerants, foam-blowing agents etc.

Diethyl ether   Older name for ethoxyethane.

Ethanal   Systematic name for acetaldehyde.

Ethanamine   Systematic name for ethylamine.

Ethane CH_3-CH_3

Ethanoic acid   Systematic name for acetic acid.

Ethanol   Systematic name for ethyl alcohol, CH_3-CH_2-OH.
The alcohol in alcoholic beverages.

Ethene   Systematic name for ethylene.

Ethoxyethane   Systematic name for diethyl ether, $CH_3-CH_2-O-CH_2-CH_3$.

The substance commonly known as 'ether' and once widely used as an anaesthetic.

Ethyl acetate   Older name for ethyl ethanoate, $CH_3-CH_2-O-\underset{\underset{O}{\|}}{C}-CH_3$.

Ethyl alcohol   Older name for ethanol.

Ethylamine   Older name for ethanamine, $CH_3-CH_2-NH_2$.

Ethylene   Older name for ethene, $CH_2{=}CH_2$.

The single most important industrial chemical intermediate, in tonnage terms; monomer used in the preparation of polythene.

Ethyl ethanoate   Systematic name for ethyl acetate.

Ethyl methyl ether   Older name for methoxyethane.

Ethyne   Systematic name for acetylene.

β-Farnesene

$$CH_3-\underset{\underset{CH_3}{|}}{C}{=}CH-CH_2-CH_2-\underset{\underset{CH_3}{|}}{C}{=}CH-CH_2-CH_2-\underset{\underset{CH_2}{\|}}{C}-CH{=}CH_2$$

The *trans* isomer is an aphid alarm pheromone.

1-Fluorobutane $CH_3-CH_2-CH_2-CH_2-F$

Fluoroethane CH_3-CH_2-F

1-Fluorohexane $CH_3-(CH_2)_5-F$

Fluoromethane CH_3-F

Fluoromethylamine $F-CH_2-NH_2$

1-Fluoropentane $CH_3-(CH_2)_4-F$

1-Fluoropropane $CH_3-CH_2-CH_2-F$

2-Fluoropropane $CH_3-CHF-CH_3$

Fluorotrichloromethane   Systematic name for Freon 11, CCl_3F.

Formaldehyde   Older name for methanal, $CH_2{=}O$.

Formic acid   Older name for methanoic acid, $H\underset{\underset{O}{\|}}{C}-OH$.

Freon 11   Trade name for fluorotrichloromethane, CCl_3F.
Used as a refrigerant, aerosol propellant and foam-blowing agent.

Freon 12   Trade name for dichlorodifluoromethane, CCl_2F_2.
Used as a refrigerant, aerosol propellant and foam-blowing agent.

Freon 22   Trade name for chlorodifluoromethane, $CHClF_2$.
Used as a refrigerant in deep-freezes.

(+)Glucose   A sugar that occurs widely in nature.

(−)Glucose   The unnatural optical isomer of the naturally occurring sugar, (+)glucose.

Glycidol $\underset{\diagdown O \diagup}{CH_2-CH_2}-CH_2-OH$

(−)Glycidyl butyrate $CH_2-CH-CH_2-O-C-CH_2-CH_2-CH_3$

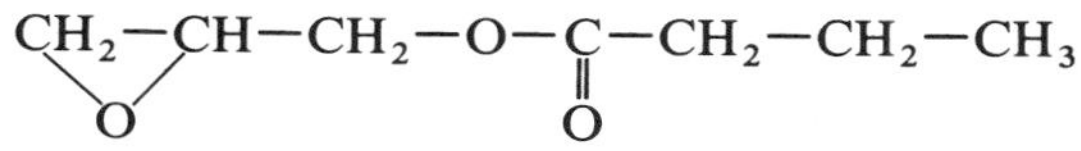

A chiral intermediate for the synthesis of drugs such as the so-called 'beta-blockers'.

Glycine NH_2-CH_2-C-OH

A naturally occurring amino acid.

Heptane $CH_3-(CH_2)_5-CH_3$

Heptan-2-one $CH_3-(CH_2)_4-C-CH_3$

An ant alarm pheromone.

Hexadecan-1-ol $CH_3-(CH_2)_{15}-OH$.

Hexamethylene diamine Older name for hexane-1,6-diamine.

Hexanal $CH_3-(CH_2)_4-CH=O$

Hexan-1-amine Systematic name for *n*-hexylamine.

Hexane $CH_3-(CH_2)_4-CH_3$

Hexane-1,6-diamine $NH_2-(CH_2)_6-NH_2$

One of the two monomers used for making nylon-6,6.

Hexanedioic acid Systematic name for adipic acid,

$HO-C-(CH_2)_4-C-OH$.

One of the two monomers used for making nylon-6,6.

Hexan-1-ol Systematic name for *n*-hexyl alcohol $CH_3-(CH_2)_5-OH$.

Hex-2-enal $CH_3-CH_2-CH_2-CH=CH-CH=O$

The *trans* isomer is an ant alarm pheromone.

***n*-Hexyl alcohol** Older name for hexan-1-ol.

***n*-Hexylamine** Older name for hexan-1-amine, $CH_3-(CH_2)_5-NH_2$.

Iodomethane CH_3-I

(+)Lactic acid $CH_3-CH-C-OH$

The naturally occurring optical isomer; formed in the muscles during vigorous exercise.

(+)Lactose A sugar present in milk.

Methadone A synthetic analgesic that can be used as a replacement for heroin in the treatment of drug addicts.

Methanal Systematic name for formaldehyde.

Methanamine Systematic name for methylamine.

Methane CH_4

The chief constituent of North Sea gas.

Methanoic acid   Systematic name for formic acid.

Methanol   Systematic name for methyl alcohol, CH_3-OH.

Methanol is manufactured on a vast scale for a variety of industrial uses. It is highly toxic—low doses cause blindness, larger amounts are fatal—and is mixed with ethanol (the alcohol in alcoholic drinks), along with other contaminants, to make the alcohol undrinkable, giving the mixture known as methylated spirits.

Methoxyethane   Systematic name for ethyl methyl ether, $CH_3-O-CH_2-CH_3$.

1-Methoxypropane   Systematic name for methyl *n*-propyl ether, $CH_3-O-CH_2-CH_2-CH_3$.

2-Methoxypropane   Systematic name for *iso*-propyl methyl ether,

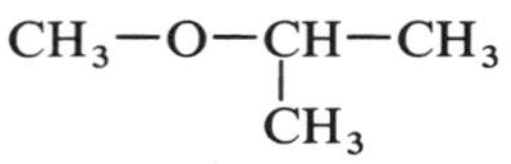

$$CH_3-O-\underset{\underset{CH_3}{|}}{CH}-CH_3$$

Methyl alcohol   Older name for methanol.

Methylamine   Older name for methanamine, CH_3-NH_2.

Methylamine is manufactured from methanol and is also produced by stale fish, contributing to its characteristic unpleasant odour.

4-Methylheptan-3-one

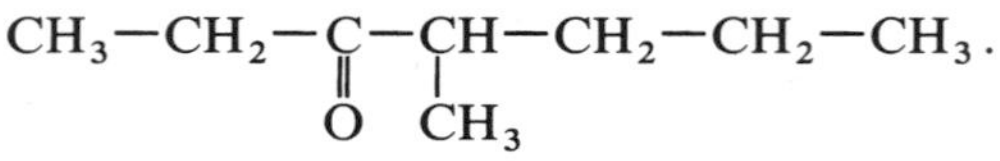

$$CH_3-CH_2-\underset{\underset{O}{\|}}{C}-\underset{\underset{CH_3}{|}}{CH}-CH_2-CH_2-CH_3.$$

An ant alarm pheromone.

3-Methylhexane

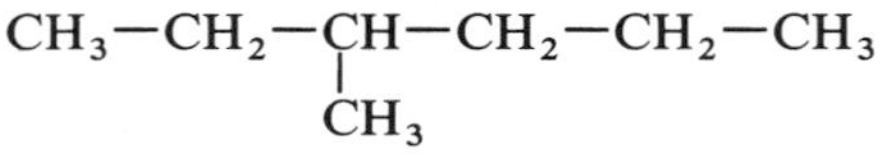

$$CH_3-CH_2-\underset{\underset{CH_3}{|}}{CH}-CH_2-CH_2-CH_3$$

2-Methylpropan-1-ol   Systematic name for *iso*-butyl alcohol,

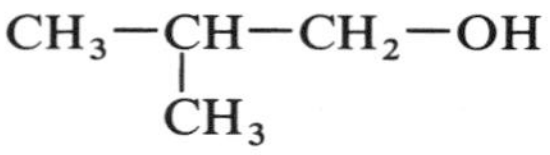

$$CH_3-\underset{\underset{CH_3}{|}}{CH}-CH_2-OH$$

2-Methylpropan-2-ol   Systematic name for *tert*-butyl alcohol,

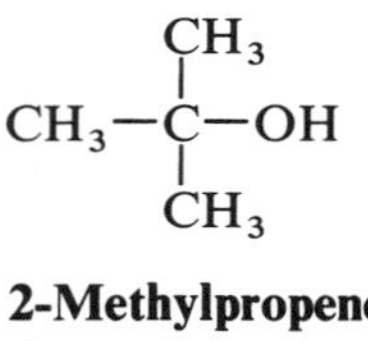

$$CH_3-\overset{\overset{CH_3}{|}}{\underset{\underset{CH_3}{|}}{C}}-OH$$

2-Methylpropene $$CH_3-\underset{\underset{CH_3}{|}}{C}=CH_2$$

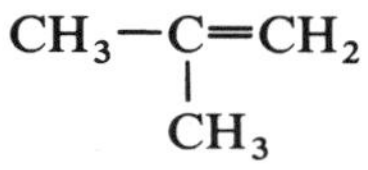

Methyl *n*-propyl ether   Older name for 1-methoxypropane.

(+)Monosodium glutamate

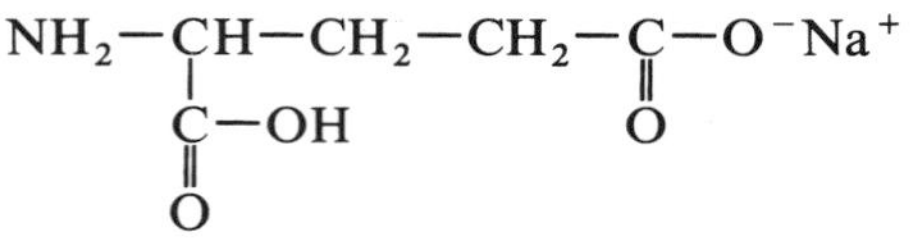

$$NH_2-\underset{\underset{\underset{O}{\|}}{\underset{C-OH}{|}}}{CH}-CH_2-CH_2-\underset{\underset{O}{\|}}{C}-O^-Na^+$$

Known as MSG, the sodium salt of a naturally occurring amino acid and used extensively as a flavour-enhancing agent.

Nonane $CH_3-(CH_2)_7-CH_3$.

Nonan-2-one $CH_3-(CH_2)_6-\underset{\underset{O}{\|}}{C}-CH_3$

A bee alarm pheromone.

Nylon   A generic term for a synthetic polyamide.

Nylon-6   A synthetic polyamide with repeating unit

$-NH-(CH_2)_5-\underset{\underset{O}{\|}}{C}-$

Nylon-6,6   A synthetic polyamide with repeating unit

$-NH-(CH_2)_6-NH-\underset{\underset{O}{\|}}{C}-(CH_2)_4-\underset{\underset{O}{\|}}{C}-$

Nylon-6,10   A synthetic polyamide with repeating unit

$-NH-(CH_2)_6-NH-\underset{\underset{O}{\|}}{C}-(CH_2)_8-\underset{\underset{O}{\|}}{C}-$

Octane $CH_3-(CH_2)_6-CH_3$

Octan-1-ol $CH_3-(CH_2)_7-OH$

Penta-1,3-diene $CH_3-CH=CH-CH=CH_2$

Pentan-1-amine   Systematic name for *n*-pentylamine.

Pentane $CH_3-(CH_2)_3-CH_3$

Pentan-1-ol   Systematic name for *n*-pentyl alcohol, $CH_3-(CH_2)_4-OH$.

Pentan-2-one $CH_3-CH_2-CH_2-\underset{\underset{O}{\|}}{C}-CH_3$

Pentan-3-one $CH_3-CH_2-\underset{\underset{O}{\|}}{C}-CH_2-CH_3$

***n*-Pentyl alcohol**   Older name for pentan-1-ol.

***n*-Pentylamine**   Older name for pentan-1-amine $CH_3-(CH_2)_4-NH_2$.

Phenol $Ph-OH$ (Ph = phenyl group, C_6H_5)

Formerly known as carbolic acid, used as a strong general disinfectant and as an important industrial intermediate, for example in the formation of the synthetic resin known as Bakelite.

(−)Phenylalanine

$NH_2-\underset{}{\overset{\overset{\displaystyle Ph}{|}}{C}H}-\underset{\underset{O}{\|}}{C}-OH$

A naturally occurring amino acid; it has the L configuration.

(+)Phenylalanine   The unnatural optical isomer of the naturally occurring amino acid.

Polyester   A synthetic polymer in which the monomeric units are joined by ester links.

Polyethene   Systematic name for polyethylene ('polythene').

Polyethylene   Older name for polyethene ('polythene'); repeating unit $-CH_2-CH_2-$.

Polypropene   Systematic name for polypropylene.

Polypropylene Older name for polypropene; repeating unit

$$-CH_2-\underset{\underset{\displaystyle CH_3}{|}}{CH}-$$

Polythene Common name for polyethene (polyethylene).

Propanal $CH_3-CH_2-CH=O$

Propan-1-amine Systematic name for *n*-propylamine.

Propane $CH_3-CH_2-CH_3$
Used in liquefied form as a fuel, for example as LPG (liquefied petroleum gas) in certain vehicles.

Propan-1-ol Systematic name for *n*-propyl alcohol, $CH_3-CH_2-CH_2-OH$

Propan-2-ol Systematic name for *iso*-propyl alcohol, $CH_3-\underset{\underset{\displaystyle OH}{|}}{CH}-CH_3$

Propanone Systematic name for acetone.

Propene Systematic name for propylene.

***iso*-Propyl alcohol** Older name for propan-2-ol.

***n*-Propyl alcohol** Older name for propan-1-ol.

***n*-Propylamine** Older name for propan-1-amine, $CH_3-CH_2-CH_2-NH_2$.

Propylene Older name for propene, $CH_3-CH=CH_2$.
Monomer for the manufacture of polypropylene.

***iso*-Propyl methyl ether** Older name for 2-methoxypropane.

Propyne $CH_3-C\equiv CH$

(+)Serine $HO-CH_2-\underset{\underset{\displaystyle NH_2}{|}}{CH}-\underset{\underset{\displaystyle O}{\|}}{C}-OH$

A naturally occurring amino acid; it has the L configuration.

Styrene $Ph-CH=CH_2$ (Ph = phenyl group, C_6H_5)
Monomer for the manufacture of polystyrene.

ACKNOWLEDGEMENTS

Grateful acknowledgement is made to the following sources for permission to use material in these Units:

Figure 1 Mansell Collection; *Figure 2* Middlesex Hospital, London; *Figure 3* courtesy of Intel Corporation (UK) Ltd; *Figure 4* courtesy of British Gas; *Figures 19 and 20* courtesy of the Agricultural and Food Research Council; *Figure 27* courtesy of Genzyme Fine Chemicals, Haverhill.

Plate 1 courtesy of Royal Holloway and New Bedford College, University of London/Bridgeman Art Library; *Plate 3* Tony Stone Worldwide; *Plate 4* courtesy of Firemaster Extinguisher Ltd., London; *Plate 5* NASA; *Plate 9* courtesy of Courtaulds Ltd; *Plate 10* courtesy of Times Furnishing.

Cartoons: *pp. 6, 17, 24, 51, 65, 75 and 88* Sidney Harris, New Haven; *p. 94* 1974, *American Scientist*, reprinted by permission of Henry R. Martin.

The author wishes to thank particularly Dr. G. N. Robinson of Telford College, Edinburgh, for her many stimulating comments and suggestions made during the writing of these Units.

INDEX FOR UNITS 17–18

PLATE 1 Victorian life: *The Railway Station*, painted by William Powell Frith. The scene is Paddington Station, London, in 1862.

PLATE 2 Nowadays, we take it for granted that clothes are available in virtually any colour or shade.

PLATE 3 Hot-air balloons and sailboats. Hot-air balloon envelopes and sails such as these are made from nylon or polyester.

PLATE 4   Portable fire extinguisher containing 'BCF' (bromochloro-difluoromethane) of the type sold for use in cars and other vehicles. This type of extinguisher is particularly effective for fires involving petrol or other fuels.

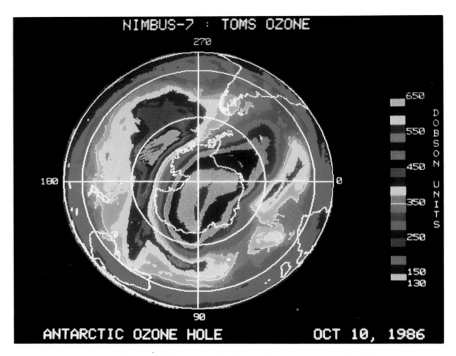

PLATE 5   False-colour satellite map of the total ozone in the Southern Hemisphere, taken on 10 October 1986, showing the 'ozone hole' that has appeared each spring (September to November in the Southern Hemisphere) over the Antarctic in recent years. The size of the 'hole' (that is, the region where the depletion is greater than was normal before 1979) corresponds to the area of the USA. The area of greatest depletion (shown as the dark blue strip just below the intersection of the two axes) corresponds to an ozone column of 163 Dobson units, or a depletion of 40% compared with 1979. (This picture was produced using data from the Total Ozone Mapping Spectrometer (TOMS) instrument aboard the Nimbus-7 satellite, which monitors the ozone over the entire Earth every day.)

PLATE 6   Apparatus to show the rotation of plane-polarized light by optically active substances. From left to right it comprises a sodium lamp, a polarizer (a piece of Polaroid sheet in a holder), a cylindrical cell containing the sample, and a second polarizer in its holder.

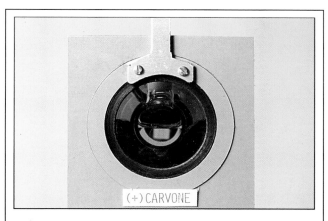

PLATE 7a   With the polarizers crossed, no light is transmitted through the (empty) upper half of the cell. However, because the (+)carvone has rotated the plane of polarization, light is transmitted through the lower half of the cell.

PLATE 7b   With the front polarizer rotated *anticlockwise* through about 60°, light is transmitted through both halves of the cell.

PLATE 7c   With the front polarizer rotated *clockwise* through about 60°, light is transmitted through the upper half of the cell. However, because the (+)carvone has rotated the plane of polarization by about 60°, no light is transmitted through the lower half of the cell.

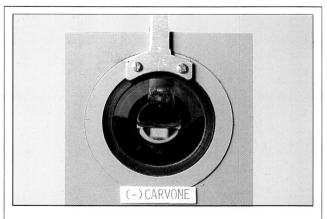

PLATE 8a   With the polarizers crossed, no light is transmitted through the (empty) upper half of the cell. However, because the (−)carvone has rotated the plane of polarization, light is transmitted through the lower half of the cell.

PLATE 8b   With the front polarizer rotated *clockwise* through about 60°, light is transmitted through both halves of the cell.

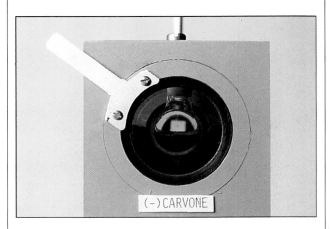

PLATE 8c   With the front polarizer rotated *anticlockwise* through about 60°, light is transmitted through the upper half of the cell. However, because the (−)carvone has rotated the plane of polarization by about 60°, no light is transmitted through the lower half of the cell.

PLATE 9 Garments made from Courtelle, an acrylic fibre (top) and from a polyester/cotton mixture (bottom). Textiles made from mixtures of synthetic and natural fibres combine the hardwearing and 'easy care' qualities of the former with the more comfortable characteristics of the latter.

PLATE 10 Carpets made from (left) nylon-6,6 and (right) a mixture of polypropylene and polyester. As with clothes, carpets are often made from mixtures of synthetic fibres and wool, and for much the same reasons: the combination of hard-wearing qualities of the former and the more luxurious 'feel' of the latter.